3-15-08

For Michelle:

Any friend of Gail's
is a friend of mine - This
book is right up your alley -
I could tell you are a white
Light being and that makes
you and I kindred spirits -
Enjoy this book and allow
its message to help you shine
your Light & spread your Love
to all who cross your path -

With Light & Love

JY Jordan

Teachings for a New World

---

*The heart-warming story of human
potential that ignites a
spiritual connection
between you and your loved ones.*

Teachings
for a
New World

*The heart-warming story of
human potential that ignites
a spiritual connection
between you and your loved ones.*

By
Steve D'Annunzio and Jeff Locker

White Light Press
New York

White Light Press
P.O. Box 23
Hewlett, New York 11557

D'Annunzio, Steve and Locker, Jeff
Teachings for a New World: The heart-warming story of
human potential that ignites a spiritual connection between
you and your loved ones / by Steve D'Annunzio and
Jeff Locker. –1st ed.

ISBN 0-9658294-5-6

    1. Self-help   I. Title
    2. Spirituality
    3. Behavior Modification

Library of Congress Catalog Card Number 97-60995

Printed in the United States of America
First Edition: November, 1998

Cover designed by DISC MAKERS
Typesetting and layout by Susan Chaffee

DEDICATION

To Allison Grace Locker and Alicia Rayne Pixley D'Annunzio, both of whom were born during the writing of this book. The energy of these two Goddesses inspired and guided us throughout our writing process.

This book is also dedicated to our families, spiritual guides and mentors whose support and guidance made this book possible.

And to you, Dear Reader, for your desire to remember the miraculous divinity of God within you.

Contents

Introduction

The book you are about to read talks about two separate stories of human possibility. They take place in very different times, but are united by a similarity of the human spirit and a commitment to overcome adversity and move out of the "survive" mode into the "thrive" mode. These two stories revolve around seven Teachings handed down through time that empower you to build your self- mastery in dealing with the constant challenges and opportunities the universe offers. Each Teaching deals with a different element of life and as you implement them, you experience increased joy and fulfillment. They differ from many complex principles sometimes associated with other self help books. This book is easy to grasp and simple to use. The Teachings build upon one another to create a road map that leads you to your next level of evolution.

To get the greatest value from reading this book, all that is necessary is for you to read with an open mind. Remain open to new possibilities and new realities, and to the best of your ability suspend your preconceptions of the way you believe things have to be. To paraphrase Albert Einstein, The same level of thinking that got you to this point in your life, can't possibly be the same level of thinking to get you to the next point in your life. We hope that some parts of this book will stretch your imagination, and if this happens we are honored, for once the mind has been expanded it can never go back to what it was. Our intent in writing this book is to help you achieve the fullest expression of yourself. To help you accomplish this we have included two very powerful study guides. Study Guide One is designed to aid parents in providing greater wisdom and practical application of the teachings as they are reading the book to their younger children or discussing it with their older ones. The questions in this study guide are most effective when asked at the end of each chapter. Study Guide Two is designed to help you the reader get the most value and benefit from applying the wisdom of the teachings into your real life's situations. The questions in this study guide work best after you have finished reading the entire book.

Enjoy this story and let it's contents be our gift to you, your family, friends and business associates.

Jeff Locker and Steve D'Annunzio

PART ONE

The Teachings in
the Old World

1
Return of the White Buffalo

On the day the child was born, the White Buffalo came back to The People. The White Buffalo had not been seen for one hundred and eight cycles of the harvest moon. It was known to The People that when this sacred sign from The Great Spirit appeared, it would signal the beginning of a new time. This new life would be the dawn of the Rainbow Tribe. This time period would begin with tremendous upheaval and pain, as with any birth, and would culminate with all nations, colors, and creeds living in harmony upon the earth.

It was a powerful myth handed down by word of mouth from as long ago as any elder could remember, and while most of The People were overjoyed, some were fearful with uncertainty. The Grandfathers would gather in the Great Tepee and speak of the coming of the White

Buffalo with reverence and hope. Great Bear was the Elder grandfather and he would speak of the buffalo as the sustainer of The People. He said, "The buffalo feeds us, clothes us, and gives us skins for our shelter. From his bones we make needles and hooks to sew and catch fish. The buffalo is the sacred provider of our people. But, my sons, when the White Buffalo appears, you do not kill it, for this would be very bad. The White Buffalo feeds new hope in our hearts, clothes our spirit for the next world, the real world beyond this world we think is real, but is only a dream. No, my sons, the White Buffalo is a special holy sign of change to our people."

The chief of the tribe was named Wolf with a Heart. He was strong and fierce like a wolf, but had compassion and a kind heart. The former chief was his father, Laughing Wolf, who had been killed by a warlike tribe from the South. Though some of the people weren't sure one so young could lead them wisely, Wolf with a Heart ascended to the position of chief at age twenty-two.

One day while out hunting, Wolf with a Heart followed a deer into a stand of pine trees that were so thick, he lost sight of the deer. He then smelled the familiar musky odor of the buffalo, but his mind wouldn't accept that there could be buffalo in a dense pine forest. The buffalo was a plains animal, how could a herd be in the forest? At that moment he heard a tremendous crashing sound as if a mountain was pushing its way through the trees. Wolf with a Heart instantly threw his bow over his head and grabbed a low limb, swinging his feet over the branch. He quickly climbed another branch up the large pine tree as his mind reeled trying to put together what could possibly be creating the terrible sound that was almost on top of him.

Only a few feet away from him, he gasped as he glimpsed the most majestic creature he had ever seen. The White Buffalo was somehow side-stepping the large trunked trees, and running over the smaller saplings. As it stampeded directly beneath Wolf with a Heart, the chief realized he had never seen an animal that big, and his heart was bursting with pride as he recalled the prophecy and its implications.

* * *

Crystal Eagle Woman screamed in pain as, in a rush of blood and fluid, her son was born. She began to cry at about the same time the infant took its first breaths and began crying also. She cried for her husband, who had ridden off with their chief two months before, never to be seen again. She cried that he would never see his son, hold him, teach him to hunt and ride, and her sadness was quelled only by the sight of her shining baby boy. Alone, she wrapped him in buffalo skin, put him to her breast, and lay back into the tall grass to rest her weary body. It was late morning, and she decided to sleep for a while. When she felt strong enough, she would bring the baby back to the village for The People to see.

The sun was high in the sky when she awoke. She gathered herself and her baby, and was just at the edge of the village of tepees when she heard a commotion as people were excitedly gathering around a lone rider who had just entered the encampment. She slowly and weakly walked over to the throng and listened in amazement as Wolf with a Heart proudly related his story. As he did so, the grandfathers held their arms outstretched, palms upward, as they gazed into the heavens, praising and thanking the Great Spirit. Young braves whooped and hollered as they understood this as the sign that was the answer to their prayers.

The People believed that all life, and nature, the four-legged and two-legged creatures, the weather, the trees, the buffalo, EVERYTHING, was completely and inexorably connected. As such, they were taught to live life in an interrelated way - that there were no accidents in their world - all events happened for a specific reason as part of the Great Spirit's plan.

As Crystal Eagle Woman heard Wolf with a Heart's story, she screamed and held her newborn son over her head for all to see.

The crowd became silent, and then began to cheer. The relevance of the birth of this boy to the recently widowed woman at the same time as the White Buffalo's appearance made this child holy and special.

Wolf with a Heart walked over to the new mother and said respectfully, "Crystal Eagle Woman has suffered greatly these past few moons. Great Spirit has taken her husband home, but has given her and us an incredible gift in the form of her newborn son, born on the day of the White Buffalo's return. This child harkens a new vision as a time of awakening and growth that is necessary for the good of The People. As we believe - all happens for a reason. I believe this child will grow to be a great teacher and leader of us all." He looked respectfully into the mother's eyes and she smiled bravely. "With his mother's permission, I name him White Buffalo."

Even when White Buffalo was a young boy, the People knew that he was different. He would sing and dance by himself and for his mother. At age eight, he wasn't interested in learning to hunt and ride as much as he enjoyed sitting with the elders and taking part in their philosophical and sometimes childishly humorous discussions. He seemed to be born with a working knowledge and understanding of the doctrines and morals of The People.

One day, he shocked the grandfathers and Great Bear in particular, as the discussion was about telling the truth. One elder, Black Crow, shared his own point of view by saying, "You must not tell a liar the truth, for he will take advantage of you. While telling the truth is a good rule, it's acceptable to lie to the liars." At this point, White Buffalo asked if he could speak. Great Bear nodded, and the boy said, "Black Crow, do you tell the truth?" The elder was visibly perturbed by the question.

"I always speak the truth unless I know I'm dealing with someone who has a deceitful reputation."

"By deceiving them, haven't you turned yourself into what they are?" asked the boy.

"No my son," said Black Crow laughing nervously. "You're too young, you wouldn't understand such things."

White Buffalo continued speaking, "You are my elder and I respect you, but if you lie, you are a liar. You have then become the thing you despised. How can this be right?"

"Be quiet boy!" said the elder barely able to contain himself. At that moment, Great Bear put his hands up in the air commanding everyone's silence. "The boy speaks the wisdom of the grandfathers. A liar is a person who is yet to learn the lesson and value of honesty. We can never teach that person this important lesson by doing what he does. The best course of action is to not keep company with liars. Eventually, their loneliness would teach them that their dishonesty has pushed others away, and they would then try truth as a means of earning respect and friendship. Truth is the language of the Great Spirit, while lies are the tools of greedy men. If one really honors truth, you can never justify lying."

With these words, Great Bear was able to teach an important lesson that was revealed by the simple but powerfully direct questions that came from the boy. Stories began to circulate around the village about the boy's interactions with the elders.

As these stories spread, two factions emerged in the village. One group thought White Buffalo was a great visionary, and teacher. This group included the chief and the elders, so it was the larger of the two groups.

The other, smaller group, feared him, as many people fear what they do not understand. They said, "It's unnatural for a boy not to be interested in hunting, fishing and riding. Who is he to tell the elders how to think, anyway? And can you believe Wolf with a Heart actually consults him on some decisions that affect us all?"

Unaffected by this opinion of him, White Buffalo continued to grow up with learning and teaching as the natural way of his personality. On a hot summer's day, instead of hunting deer, he would sit by a pond with an apple, hoping to feed the animals. When a deer would cautiously approach to drink, White Buffalo would bite into the apple, the deer would smell it, and sensing the boy's good intentions, the deer would eat right out of his hand. Soon, rabbits, prairie hens and most creatures came to trust him in this way. The young man would study the way of these four-legged creatures, and also the habits of the winged ones. He made mental notes of plants and flowers that they ate when they were sick. Once he noticed an abnormal growth on the throat of a pony he had nicknamed Spotted Colt. Every day the growth was getting larger, and Spotted Colt became more ill and less friendly. Then the following week, White Buffalo noticed the growth going down and wondered why. He followed the colt to a small hidden meadow where the pony grazed from a strange yellow flower. Each day he did so, the growth slowly went away as the pony returned to its friendly disposition. The following month, his mother, Crystal Eagle Woman, came down with a sore throat. Then she lost her voice completely, and developed a painful lump in her throat. White Buffalo went to the hidden meadow and plucked several of the yellow flowered plants, and made a tea of them for his mother to drink. Within three days, her voice returned and the lump disappeared. Incidents like this became commonplace and The People began to look to him as a healer.

He had a sharp, agile mind that included incredible memory recall, so he easily remembered what herbs to use for each specific ailment. Whenever a member of the tribe heard of a new remedy, White Buffalo sought that person out to learn about it.

The more his knowledge as a healer and teacher grew, the wider the division between the two factions grew also.   Those who believed in him were more vehement about his abilities, as those who feared him became more firmly entrenched in staying away from him.   Though he was oblivious to these goings on, his mother became concerned.   One day she asked him to talk to her about the situation.   She asked what he thought about the two factions. He said, "Mother, I cannot control what people think about me or about anything for that matter.   I can only control how I choose to react to these things.   If those who are suspicious of me were open minded enough to approach me about their concerns, I could easily allay their fears.   Since they are closed minded, this isn't possible.   While I care about them as people of our tribe, I don't care about their opinion of me, because it is really based on ignorance and, therefore, means nothing. As long as those who mistrust me don't limit my working to positively and peacefully help our village, I am unaffected by them and their opinions."

Crystal Eagle Woman felt the wisdom in her son's words, but still had concerns.   "I don't know where your wisdom comes from, my son, and though it makes sense, I still fear for your safety. For me, would you make a small effort and try to talk to some of those you know fear you? If only they would speak with you, I'm sure they would come to see you as most of us do." White Buffalo said, "Mother, if it makes you happy, I will do so."

At this point in his life, White Buffalo was twelve years old. He was a smallish boy with a thin face, and long black hair that he wore in a braid down the middle of his back, as did most boys in the village. He had light brown skin and piercing brown eyes that were intense yet compassionate.   Though small for his age, he had a powerful musculature, and had he been inclined to, possessed the physical potential to be a fierce warrior.

Because of his vow to his mother, he decided to seek out someone in the faction of people who mistrusted him and find the right person to teach him riding. Though he was more interested in herbs and philosophy than hunting and the bow, riding a pony was a good skill to have, especially since he wasn't very proficient at it. He also believed that if he went to them seeking their knowledge, they would feel more comfortable being around him, and less threatened by his metaphysical prowess.

After some thought on the matter, White Buffalo decided that Stone Hawk was the perfect person to approach. Stone Hawk was two years older than he, big and strong for his age, an excellent rider and bowman who already hunted with the braves and had killed his first buffalo by himself.

Stone Hawk was a handsome boy, tall and powerfully built, but possessed a very average mentality. He stammered when he spoke and was slow to learn. Though respected for his strength, he was an easy target for teasing by the other braves. His only defense was to fight his way out of these situations, and consequently his physical strength grew while his mental powers dwindled.

Stone Hawk's parents were simple minded people and had raised their son in the traditional ways of The People. They opposed anything that signaled change, even if that change was for the better. They were loud and outspoken, of average intelligence and skill, and did not hide their dislike of White Buffalo. Since they didn't understand him, they believed his intention was to work his way into the hierarchy of the ruling council, where his gentle ways would soften the defenses of The People. This, they believed, would eventually lead to their defeat and enslavement at the hands of a warlike tribe.

Stone Hawk's parents became the loudest voice in the faction of people who didn't trust the young healer. It is the way of things for a child to follow his parents' teachings whether good or bad, so he also disliked and mistrusted White Buffalo.

White Buffalo knew that if he approached Stone Hawk as a student, the elder boy might relish the opportunity to be in a position of control over him, and hopefully a friendship could develop. Either way, White Buffalo believed that only good could come from his attempt, if not in creating a new friend, then in learning to ride. Even if Stone Hawk refused to be his riding teacher, White Buffalo would show his humility in the eyes of the villagers by asking help from one who openly denounced him.

White Buffalo went to the family tepee of Stone Hawk and tapped on the buffalo skin that was covering the entrance way. When the older boy opened the flap, he saw White Buffalo and he said with disdain, "What do you want?" White Buffalo said, "Stone Hawk, you are one of the best riders in the village, and as I am unskilled at riding, I would be honored if you would teach me the ways of the pony and riding." "An an an honor?" stammered Stone Hawk, somewhat amazed. "Yes," replied White Buffalo. "Then I accept your proposal, but you must do exactly as I tell you or I will instantly drop you as a student!" said Stone Hawk confidently. Then he added, "Let us begin at once!"

The would-be teacher came sprinting out of his tepee toward the rear of his pony which was roped to a long pole standing straight up out of the ground. He leaped over the tail and hind quarters of the pony, which jumped back startled. With a quick flick of his wrist, Stone Hawk undid the loose knot that secured his pony to the pole and rode crazily around White Buffalo whooping and hollering with joy.

He untied one of his father's ponies and handed the rope to White Buffalo, who stood there sheepishly, then tried to get on. He could not.

Laughing at first, the teacher dismounted and taught the student how to mount the pony, and after a few tries, he was successful. In those days, they rode with no saddle, sometimes riding on a blanket thrown over the pony's back, but mostly bareback.

Stone Hawk was an excellent rider, but an impatient teacher. "You ride like a woman," was his favorite teasing remark when he felt White Buffalo wasn't living up to his expectations. No matter how badly Stone Hawk chided his student, White Buffalo never got angry or quit. They agreed to meet at dawn each day for riding, and regardless of the previous day's events, good or bad, White Buffalo was there.

After three moons of daily riding, the student had become a capable rider. After three more moons, White Buffalo was almost as good as his teacher. Also, a different dynamic appeared in their relationship. White Buffalo had earned Stone Hawk's respect. When Stone Hawk saw that his student was almost as proficient as he, the teacher decided to test him. They rode through a forest of pine

trees at high speed toward the Mountain of the Broken
Rock. Then Stone Hawk led them up the mountain as fast
as the ponies would go. Up to that point, White Buffalo
stayed with him, but on the way down the mountain, the
younger rider hit loose rock, and his pony began to stumble.
White Buffalo was too out of control to be scared. As he
tried to regain his balance, the pony fell, throwing him head
first down the mountainside. He tumbled over and over,
coming to rest as his head slammed into a large rock. Stone
Hawk watched in horror as the scene unfolded. He
sprinted over to the injured rider, and called out to him to
get up, but White Buffalo was unconscious. Stone Hawk
dismounted and knelt down to lift his student's head and
came up with a handful of blood. He noticed blood coming
out of the fallen boy's mouth and began to feel sick inside.
Why had he pushed him so hard?

Stone Hawk knew he had to get White Buffalo back
to the village. He gently picked up the boy and laid him
across the back of the other pony, and began riding quickly
and cautiously back to camp.

Thoughts raced through his mind. White Buffalo
had never done anything to harm him or anyone. On the
contrary, he always wanted to help others. Stone Hawk
realized that his need to test his student stemmed from
jealousy. The only powers he had over White Buffalo were
his riding and hunting, and if the student surpassed the
teacher, how would that look to the others? Stone Hawk
felt guilty, seeing White Buffalo laying almost dead on the
back of the pony, and all because of his own pride.

2

The Teachings Unfold

White Buffalo woke up not knowing where he was. He was sitting in a grassy plateau that appeared to be on a mountain range, with clouds all around. He had never seen clouds like this, as they were purple and pink. There was music in the air, strange music coming from instruments he had never before heard.

His body felt weightless, as if he were floating. He looked at his hands and a light was emanating from them. He could see right through them to the grass behind them. He knew at once he was in the spirit world, believing he had died.

He felt compelled to speak. "Where am I? Is anyone here?" He heard thunder roar and as the wind came up, he watched the trees bend. The music increased, and swelled. Lightning flashed across the sky so close to him that he held up his hands in front of his face. As it subsided, he lowered his hands and there was a handsome smiling man standing before him.

"Hello, White Buffalo, welcome to the spirit realm. There is only peace and happiness here, as this is the place your people call the happy hunting ground." "Why am I here?" the boy asked. "To be certain you do not stray from the path which you chose when you were last here. The reason for your incarnation was to share a way for The People to evolve beyond their limitations and the self-imposed boundaries that they have created and accepted as the way things are supposed to be. Look at yourself here, you are a child of the light. You have observed your light body, as your physical body lays convalescing in a sleep state in your village on earth. You are here because we need to support you to not stray from your path as teacher and healer, and more so, to be sure you fulfill your mission by revealing new teachings to your race." The boy felt strangely attracted to and comfortable with this man. The man's countenance was straightforward and sincere, and the boy felt as though they somehow knew each other.

"The first major lesson is to understand that we have eternal peace and happiness here because we understand the difference between right and wrong. On your world, people believe that doing something a specific way is right, and doing it the opposite way is wrong. This is not so. Now listen closely, I will share a very powerful teaching for you to build your life upon."

"Right is what ends suffering. Wrong is what creates suffering."

"If this powerful precept were honored, understood, and applied in your world, there would be only peace and joy, as there is here." "Would there then be an end of death on our planet?" asked the boy. "You ask the question incorrectly, my son," the guide continued. "Know that what you call death is an essential ingredient to life, because physicality itself is about dualities and opposites. You cannot truly learn happiness until you've experienced sadness. You cannot appreciate the light until you've been in the dark. So when you learn the difference between right and wrong, you work to end suffering and create joy. Understand that the state you call death truly is only the completion of physical life. The wondrous part is that death of the physical body is birth back into your spirit body, which is where you are right now. Isn't it extraordinary here?"

"Yes, it's incredible!" replied White Buffalo.

"While it is easy to grow in this place with only a spirit body, the real test is earning this knowledge in a physical body. This is because taking a body brings the veil of forgetfulness over you, and you have to earn your knowledge through experience and study. This application of knowledge becomes wisdom. Wisdom then leads you to your special mission - the one that only you can fulfill. Every being on your earth has a very distinct and important mission. The successful completion of one's mission creates a learning and a satisfaction that cannot be experienced in the spirit realm. This is the all important reason for taking a body. Does this make sense to you?"

"It makes perfect sense, but my mind is racing with many questions."

"You may ask your questions."

"Do all people come to this place when they die?"

"You are not dead, rather, you are here temporarily. Upon physical death, people go to the perfect place for rest and renewal. Then, when they are ready to continue their journey, other energies appear to help them with loving guidance."

"Are there others like you here?"

"I am one of the guides of the seven directions. There is a prime teaching from each of the seven directions that you must re-introduce to your people. You will first take the teachings back to your world, and live them by example. When other people see the positive results in your life, they will naturally be compelled to follow your example of their own accord."

White Buffalo said, "I understand the four directions of North, South, East, and West. What are the others?"

The guide responded, "The seven directions are North, South, East, West, Up, Down and Center. The seven directions correspond to seven energy centers in the body. As a person masters each energy center, they become more loving and increase the power and joy in their lives. When all seven energy centers, or directions, are mastered, the person becomes one with Great Spirit. When this is accomplished, all that Great Spirit can do, the master can now do."

"I am the guide of the North, direction One. The North brings the snow, which covers your world during its transition period - winter. This transition corresponds to physical death, and spiritual rebirth. The snow covers the old growth, ending its life, and as the snow melts, it waters the new life of spring. This is the teaching of birth and death, but initially of learning right from wrong. Remember, my son, life is eternal and ongoing, death is only a transition. Death happens to the body, not to YOU, for while you have a body, you are not your body. Do you understand Teaching One White Buffalo?"

"Yes, know the difference between right, which is ending suffering, from wrong, which is to create suffering," repeated the boy.

With that, the guide's spirit form began to dissipate, and White Buffalo beseechingly said, "Where are you going …?"

"Go in Peace," replied the beautiful being, and disappeared.

White Buffalo heard a tremendous thundering of hooves and turned to see an enormous black horse charging directly at him. On the horse was what appeared to be a man of iron, carrying a long spear aimed at the boy's midsection. He began running, but the horse and rider changed course to catch him, and he fell to the ground, hoping not to be killed.

The rider of iron dismounted and was laughing in a high-pitched voice, while taking off the iron headdress. White Buffalo saw that it was a woman with beautiful, long, golden hair, laughing at him! He'd never seen hair like that before.

"Why did you attack me?" he asked defiantly. "Did I attack you?" she retorted. "Well you certainly seemed about to spear me if I hadn't run away!" he exclaimed. She held her hand up. "Stop. Touch my spear." He reached out to touch it and his hand passed on through it.

"Remember where you are my brother. You are in the real world, not the dream world of bodies and physical things. Forgive me for challenging you in this manner, especially here. But my lesson is so important I needed to shock you so you NEVER forget it!"

"I am the teacher of the second direction, the South. The South represents growth, and there can be no growth in any realm without first conquering fear. This, then, is Teaching Two. Fear is the enemy - Love is the cure. Do you understand, White Buffalo?"

"Yes," he replied.

She looked long and deeply at him, sensing uncertainty. "Come with me," she said. She took the horse by the bridle, and walked with White Buffalo around a glorious hillside covered by fragrant flowers of all colors, that actually radiated light. He walked up to one that he considered most beautiful, a large purple flower with long petals and a yellow center and he inhaled deeply. He smiled at his hostess with an amazed expression, and she said to him, "Listen."

He didn't understand. "What ...?" he asked her. "Close your eyes and listen with your heart." she replied. White Buffalo did so and heard a small, almost childlike voice say, "My name is Purple Sunshine. I sense you like my fragrance. On your world, I can heal any ailment. I understand your love of herbs and flowers, so if you would like, you may pick me, but give me a moment to first withdraw my life-force energy."

White Buffalo shook his head no, thinking "I don't want you to die."

Purple Sunshine said "You already forgot

Teaching One? Nothing dies, and it's an honor to give myself to save another's life. It is our way of achieving the next heavenly step in our unfolding process."

At once he understood. Sensing she had withdrawn her life-force, he picked the flower and put it in his pocket. The golden haired woman had walked away as he conversed with Purple Sunshine, and was now standing next to a stream letting her horse take a drink.

"You see, my brother," she continued, "fear is a word that is created by taking the first four letters of the phrase it represents - False Evidence Appearing Real. Fear is false evidence appearing real. Fear is the true enemy of your world. It is the thing that stops people from achieving true happiness and freedom. Watch this scene and remember." She paused, as a hole opened up in a cloud before them. He saw himself at age eight trying to cross a log that had fallen over a stream. He remembered how scared he was of falling. He was half way across and fell into the stream. Though he was unhurt, seeing that scene over again still scared him, even now.

Golden Hair spoke again. "Your fear actually made you fall, didn't it?"

"Yes" he replied.

"When you learn to conquer fear, all powers in the universe become available to you. It is of the utmost importance, do you see?"

"Yes, fear is the enemy, love is the cure," said White Buffalo, still gazing at the cloud as the scene faded away.

They began walking as they discussed this teaching in greater detail and after a while, stopped at the base of a large reddish mountain. As the boy looked up, one of the buttes of the mountain looked like the face of an eagle. "You can see why we call this Eagle Mountain," said Golden Hair.

"This mountain is alive as are all things, but it is ancient, much older than any physical thing in your universe. Lay your hands on her face and you will feel what I mean."

White Buffalo laid his hands and head against the rock wall. He instantly felt warmth and renewal. He sensed a deep musical tone, so low that at first he wasn't sure it was there, but then it became more noticeable. It was the deepest tone he had ever heard, and it sounded like 'Oooo'. He tapped on the rock with his knuckles and it sounded hollow. Laying his cheek against the rock face again, the 'Oooo' sound evolved with 'Oooowelcome'.

White Buffalo, once again slightly startled, turned around to ask a question of Golden Hair but the boy was alone. He turned back to the stone wall. Where his hands and face had momentarily touched the rock wall, there were glowing pinkish light outlines of exactly where skin met rock. He felt guided to put his hands and face back onto the same spots and did so. In his heart he heard, "Call me Eagle, or Mountain, but I am Mother. We cannot talk if you use mind. You must use heart. I differ from other life. I am simple. I am direct. No past-future, only now. Those at the top of the mountain see the sunrise first. This is the sunrise of the self in union with Great Spirit. Sunrise is East, which is the direction of this teaching. Come up to the top of the mountain to experience the sunrise.

White Buffalo knew this meant for him to climb the mountain. He felt utter and total reverence. Though there was no clearly defined path, at each possible decision as to which way to go, he heard in his heart "Yes, No or Here" as guiding words, knowing it was Mother.

At last he came to the summit. There was a circle of twelve trees. The color in the air was golden and the music was soft, distant and inspiring. In the center of the twelve trees was a deer skin. The boy sat on it.

From his heart he heard, "You have a big heart and a big mission. It is the time of ascension on your planet. Ascension is the sunrise of the true self within the body. It begins with self-love and then moves to self-mastery. People have become lazy. They are easily discouraged and they have little discipline. Mother's message of self is simple. Do what has to be done when it has to be done. That is all. Under you are my seven children. Take them with you for they will help you remember the seven directions and their teachings. That is all. I love you always - in all ways."

White Buffalo listened for more. There were no more words, only a deep tone of 'Oooo'. He sang the note of the mother for a long time. He became at one with her, and felt complete and peaceful. It was an all encompassing peace like he'd never felt before. He was sitting cross-legged, back straight, his palms facing upward with his eyes closed, breathing slowly and deeply.

He was in heaven, but he began getting a deep sense of remorse and depression at having to leave this place. He knew to fulfill his mission meant returning to his world soon, but feeling so complete here made him resist going back. Just then, something under the deerskin felt as if was poking into his backside. He lifted the skin to find seven stones, each a different color with different markings.

He remembered what Mother had said. "Under you are my seven children. Take them, for they will help you to remember the seven directions and their teachings." It made perfect sense to him that these smaller rocks would be the children of the original mountain. He put them in his pocket.

He closed his eyes and he could feel the power of the stones coursing through him. White Buffalo made mental notes of the lessons he had been taught. He wondered, almost doubted, if he would be up to the challenge of bringing these powerful concepts to his world, or if he would even remember them all.

Like a bolt of lightning the thought, "Don't worry, we will help you to remember," shot into his mind as an answer to his unspoken question. He turned to see only a pony grazing on the grass behind him. It was unusual that he did not sense the animal's presence as he was quite sensitive to the energy of others.

There was something vaguely familiar about this pony. What was it? He got to his feet and slowly approached the animal, who seemed to have absolutely no shyness or fear of him. As he petted the pony's mane, he realized that the coloring was exactly the same as his pony friend, Spotted Colt. Once again, the voice in his mind said, "That is because I am Spotted Colt's father, and I was your father's pony on earth."

White Buffalo jumped back, mouth agape. "You're talking to me in my mind?" he asked the pony incredulously.

"Yes, my friend, it is called mental telepathy," came the response, as the pony looked up for the first time directly into the boy's eyes. "You actually have done this on earth already, though you were mostly unaware that you did it. Then with Purple Sunshine, the flower essence, you did it well. Now with me, you will further hone this skill. I am the voice of millions of animal spirits here, four-legged, finned and winged creatures. We have souls, as you, but a more simply configured energy exists in our mental bodies. Despite this, we feel as intensely as you."

"In my lifetime on earth, I carried your father, who is a great being. I was the leader of the largest pony herd on the planet. When we moved, we were so large, we kicked up the wind, and made the sound of thunder."

"I am the West, bringing the winds of change. I present the teaching of Direction Four, which is Be someone who positively influences all life forms. White Buffalo, you and your people do live in harmony with most life, and we acknowledge you for that. You have learned to tap the earth gently for your needs, in this way ensuring that each tap is answered by Earth Mother and that your needs are met."

"The important piece missing in relation to Teaching Four is that your society honors mostly or exclusively men. This creates a harmonic imbalance primarily among women, and secondarily with the children. The children are the bringers of the light, what they are taught now will continue to manifest more intensely as the generations evolve. So if they currently are taught to honor men, even slightly more than women, three generations from now they will honor men much more than women. This cannot continue if love is to evolve equally on your planet."

"The spirit body of man and woman is completely equal and the same, in fact, it is one. The physical body of man is stronger than woman. The mental body of woman is stronger than man. It is that simple, and as such, they are equal, and need to be represented that way to the children. When the children see this, they will then multiply this new respect through the generations."

"Also, your race is only one of many that are evolving on your planet simultaneously. In time, strangers will come to live amongst you, and this teaching will need to be applied even more. You will need to teach these newcomers how to honor animal life as you now do, for they do not understand this concept. They currently view us as beasts of burden and food, nothing more."

"In truth, we are souls refining ourselves to one day earn the ability to take a human body on earth. This is the way of things, to always move upward on the spiral back to Great Spirit - our creator. To view us exclusively as food and servants negates our other more important role, that we are living beings trying our best to be happy, the same as you. Now, have you any questions?" asked the pony.

White Buffalo was almost afraid to think, for obviously each thought, even silly ones, would be revealed. Then he spoke out loud for he was more comfortable doing so. "Your thoughts ring true to the very core of my being, dear one. It is simple, and makes perfect sense. My question has little to do with this teaching, but I must know - is my father here?"

The pony approached the boy.

"You will know your father when you see him my friend. Now repeat Direction Four's lesson," came the telepathic response.

Disappointed, the boy said, "Be someone who positively influences all life forms."

Spotted Colt nuzzled his nose into White Buffalo's chest as tears welled up in the boy's eyes. The pony knew the boy longed to meet his father. "Your father will appear at the perfect time, and it will be soon. Were he to appear prematurely, you would not glean the teachings appropriately, which would be a grave mistake. Do not worry, my friend, for he is nearby. Now let me take you on an adventure."

3
THE REVELATION IS COMPLETE

White Buffalo climbed onto the back of Spotted Colt's father and began to ride. The boy intuitively understood that as a guide of this realm, the pony knew where to go for the next teaching to be revealed.

All concept of time had been suspended. There was constant music and shifting color here. As each teaching differed, a different infusion of color occurred. The color presences were extraordinary, as when fog is all around you, but the fog particles are gorgeous, light emitting blues and greens. The music was sometimes very faint and simplistic. In contrast, when the wind blew hard, the music intensified and became louder and more complex. The flowers, trees and even some rocks had light coming from inside of them, so the colors were not only brighter and accentuated, but seemed to vibrate.

The boy began to feel drowsy, and his head began to nod. He laid down on the pony's neck and thought of his mother. She must be worried sick. He saw a vision of her in their tepee. She was laying herbs on the body of a seemingly dead person. It was his body! He saw his face, swollen, bruised and lacerated and his arm seemed broken, as did one of his legs. His mother was washing his body, and keeping a cool cloth on his head. He could feel her pain as she believed her son to be dying. With his new found power of telepathy, he sent his mother a message. He focused all his concentration on sending this message on a ray of white light from his mind to his mother's heart.

"Dear Mother - worry not, I will not die. I am in an incredible dream, where I need to be. I will awaken soon."

His mother began crying. She took her son's swollen face in her hands, kissing his forehead. "Please come back my son, I cannot go on without you. You are my life. I would rather give my life if it meant you getting yours back. Please give me a sign that you can hear me, White Buffalo."

Her anguish overcame her, and she collapsed her head on his chest, sobbing.

White Buffalo decided he would try to momentarily re-enter his body to give her a sign. On the ray of light, he mentally sent his mother the message to hold his hand. She sat up. She did not move. The boy repeated the message and this time, his mother took his hand.

White Buffalo saw the light ray that was the mental link between he and his mother. He expressed his wish to momentarily re-enter his body to squeeze her hand, and the light ray turned into a silver cord. The boy took the cord in both hands and slowly began sliding down it. One musical note played, then started to get louder and louder. He heard a rushing sound, and the music became deafening. His body began to ache, then BOOM - a blinding flash of light and pain. At once, he could feel his mother's hand in his. Though he felt blind and dizzy, he squeezed her hand with all his might. She screamed and cried out "He will LIVE!!"

White Buffalo looked up in his mind's eye and saw the silver cord hanging from a black sky filled with stars. The cord was slowly moving away from his reach. Mustering all his intention, he mentally reached up and grabbed it with both hands, and as he touched it, he heard the musical note again, and the rush of wind. He began climbing, then felt himself effortlessly lifted along the cord upward. The cord did not proceed in a straight upward journey but moved in a spiraling configuration. He saw a light above that looked like the surface of the water when you have dived into a lake and are looking upwards as you swim toward the surface. Just as he broke through it, he felt a twitch and woke up on the back of Spotted Colt's father, who was still walking in a circle around the twelve trees at the summit's peak.

In his mind, he heard the pony say "It was very considerate of you to visit your mother and calm her anxiety. It shows great mastery to be allowed travel between realms as you have done. It means you resonate at a very high vibrational frequency with the heart of the Great Spirit. This is why you've been chosen for such an important mission."

The pony stopped at a small stream and took a drink. Realizing he was thirsty, the boy knelt down and drank out of his cupped hand. He thought he heard splashing and frolicking further downstream, so he followed the sound to find a boy playing alone. White Buffalo stopped and just watched the boy of maybe five or six for a few moments before the boy noticed him. The boy was talking to the water saying something like "You're much too fast for me here my friend, let's try it on land," and the boy giggled heartily. White Buffalo thought the boy might be a little crazy, just as the boy looked up to see him standing there.

"Hi!" said the little boy.

"Hi!" said White Buffalo, "Who are you talking to?"

"My friend, the fish, and I were playing tag," replied the boy.

"It's not kind to lie to people," replied White Buffalo.

"You just had a conversation with a pony and you doubt that I have a fish for a friend?"

White Buffalo's eyes grew wider, and then they both laughed very hard.

"Forgive me, for once again I forgot where I am."

The little boy said, "I never lie, and I know you don't either. The epidemic of lies on your planet depletes the energy of the people far more than they realize. Truth elevates the energy in the body so we can experience higher love and joy. The elevation of this life force takes us upwards in the direction of this teaching, which is Life works to the extent that you keep your word."

"As you have discovered, White Buffalo, you have a temporal physical body, and you have an eternal spiritual body, but you also possess a mental or emotional body. Think about it my friend. When you sleep, your physical body is completely shut down, right?"

"Yes."

"But you do dream," continued the boy. "And it is your mental self that experiences and acts out these dreams, sometimes so vividly that when you wake up, you wonder if they were real. That's because your mental body is real, therefore you have difficulty separating the experience from your physical reality. Truly the direction up teaches us to WAKE UP and TELL THE TRUTH."

"Now that we've proven the existence of the mental body, recognize that lies destroy the fabric of the mental body in a subtle way. Lying becomes habitual, as one lie leads to many others. The lying person then becomes constantly distracted in trying to recall what lie he told to whom, eventually trapping himself in a web of falsehood. It creates a vibration of mistrust that people can feel before they even hear the person speak. Imagine a bison bladder that you use to carry water. Also imagine that you're crossing the desert, so this water is imperative for your survival. Each lie told is like taking a cactus needle and sticking hole after hole in the water bag. The life-giving water drains out, unfortunately wasted. Each human is like that. When your mental/emotional energy is weakened through lying, a part of your life force energy drains away, unfortunately wasted. Telling lies drains away a part of your positive life force. Do you understand, my friend?" asked the boy.

"Yes I do," said White Buffalo.

The little boy looked deep into his eyes, knowing White Buffalo was telling the truth. The little one added,

"Also, establishing yourself in the truth allows you to see through others' lies."

White Buffalo nodded and said, "I understand, Life works to the extent you keep your word."

"Right!" said the little boy, as he dove into the water and swam away. "Bye!"

He heard a loud cry above him. He looked up to see a huge eagle with a white head perched on a branch in a nearby tree. In his heart, he instantly knew this was his next guide. The eagle took off, and White Buffalo followed, descending down the mountain. He entered a forest of lime green trees, like none he had ever seen. The color in the air changed to green, and he smelled a minty, piney odor that was quite pleasing. For the first time the music stopped, but he did hear drumming. The drums beat in a 4-beat, Boom-ba-ba-ba, Boom-ba-ba-ba, and so on. He found his stride down the mountain matched the drumming and this invigorated him. Every now and then, he would see the eagle sitting on a tree branch, and as soon as he noticed it, the eagle would fly off. Then the boy would proceed in that general direction until after a time he came back down to the grassy plain where he first met the beautiful, smiling man of the North, and sitting at the highest visible rock ledge on Mother was the eagle.

The eagle screamed and then began squawking like he was speaking, but White Buffalo could not understand anything. The eagle swooped down near him and then back up to its ledge, and began the squawking sounds again, but White Buffalo still couldn't understand. He decided to get back into the meditative state he had entered at the top of the mountain to search for the way to speak to his brother the

Eagle. He breathed deeply with the rhythm of the drums
and became still. He asked Great Spirit how to talk with the
eagle. Nothing came back. He remembered he had just
learned Teaching Five, and the direction was up.   He
reasoned the next lesson must be Teaching Six, which would
be the Down direction. He decided that he was still feeling
with his heart, and he needed to now listen and think with
his mind. The eagle was a hunter, always vigilant, always
in flight. The only time it came down was when it needed
to eat and to rest. This made sense to him. Down was the
direction of sustenance and rest.   Food came from the
ground. The ground is stable and solid, it creates balance.

At once the boy looked up and realized these were
not his thoughts. He was hearing Eagle Brother in his
mind. He had broken the code.

White Buffalo said, "Hello, Eagle Brother, I honor
you."

Eagle Brother's response was "Thank you, my young
friend and I offer respect to you. You are successfully
learning to use all your divine faculties. Your problem
solving skills are evolving at the same time which is
excellent. You will need all this and more if you are to
successfully spread this knowledge among The People."

"Down is the direction that corresponds to balance.
Being in balance is important as balance is the key to
achieving inner peace. The way to achieve balance is
finding a middle ground in your life combining the physical,
mental/emotional, and spiritual aspects. The first ingredient
is to have a belief system in place and working well. While
all roads lead to Great Spirit, the measure of your true path
is simple. Ask yourself while living this path, 'Do you feel
loved, and are you being loving to others?' If your belief

system does not support you according to this simple prerequisite, it is NOT a path with a heart."

"So the first piece is belief. Once you live in a belief system that you trust, it can lead you to KNOW. Knowingness is the step beyond belief, as belief is usually trusting another's opinion of something, and knowingness is the certainty that comes from your own verification of a thing. This verification may come as the result of an experiment, or it may come from observing something or even an intuitive feeling. Either way, belief stems from faith, and knowingness stems from certainty."

"You may find that a person can take on a seemingly impossible task, and against all probability, achieve success because of the strength of his belief."

"That is the exact point where belief crosses over to knowingness. Though all others believe the task can't be done, that person knows it can, and consequently transcends all limits to succeed. So, Teaching Six is To believe is great and to KNOW makes it so. Now my young friend, I sense you have questions."

"Are you saying ANY thing can be accomplished if I believe in it strongly enough?" said White Buffalo.

"Yes," replied Eagle Brother.

"That may be possible in this world, but not in the physical world," doubted the boy.

"Give a specific situation and I will show you," responded the bird.

"If I wanted to fly like you, could I learn to do it?" asked White Buffalo.

"Know that thousands of years ago, people flew in crystal ships upon your planet, and that centuries from now, people will fly again in winged ships, even to the moon and beyond. But also realize that there are certain exceptional individuals who at various times are present on your planet, and these beings have learned to transmute their physical bodies into a light body, then to a spirit body. As such, they can fly to any realm, universe, or place on your planet. While it requires much training, discipline, and practice, it is possible."

"But you see my young friend, it is the habit of your people to ask about flying before you've learned to walk. In other words, learn to love each other. That opens all doors. Once you do this, the rest of the answers all fall into place. Do you see?"

"I think so," said White Buffalo.

"Do you believe I speak the truth?" challenged Eagle Brother.

White Buffalo thought for a moment. "Of course, all things that are revealed here are the truth." He realized the one thing he knew was how much there is to know. "I know you speak the truth!" said the boy.

"Yes, and the stones in your pocket are the symbolic reminder of all you have experienced here. Guard them well, and choose wisely, for what you believe will manifest."

Then Eagle Brother swooped down toward the boy. White Buffalo held his arm out and the huge bird landed firmly on his arm. The talons squeezed his arm tightly almost breaking the skin, but not doing so. "I must share with you one more important piece, my brother," said the eagle. "When you need the energy of a certain teaching to give you additional power, face in that direction and hold the corresponding stone to your heart. Think of the appropriate color, and KNOW that the desired energy is on the way to you immediately. This is important. You are loved more than you can know." Then Eagle Brother flew off.

The drumming stopped and one soft thin tone took its place. White Buffalo was alone, but did not feel lonely. He dug into his pocket and pulled out the stones.

The red stone had a lightning bolt on it. He remembered that this symbolized the teaching of the North.

The orange stone had a scale on it. It represented South.

The yellow stone had a sun, which obviously meant the dawn. This happens in the East.

The green stone had three white waves, which at first confused him. Then he realized it represented the wind, which comes from the West.

The blue stone had an arrow with a horizontal line intersecting it like a cross, and he instinctively knew this stone represented Up.

The indigo stone had a circle on top, with an arrow extending downward from the circle, which symbolized Down.

That left the purple stone. It had a circle with a dot in the Center of the circle.

He concluded that this stone represented the Center. He looked forward to this teaching, as it must be powerful if it represented the centering principle.

He sat in quiet anticipation and waited. Nothing came. He started thinking about all the incredible events that led up to this moment. His injury, waking up in a heavenly place of purity and knowledge. The incredible teachings and his guides, the smiling man, golden hair, young boy, pony guide, Great Mother, and Eagle Brother. He laid the stones out one by one and reflected on each guide and teaching. As these powerful thoughts took shape, the music formed into an intensely forceful song that began to crescendo. Many colors became visible and began to swirl around him, slowly at first, then gathering momentum. As he summed up all his experiences and lessons, he was left staring at the purple stone. His mind became still. Simultaneously the song ended, except for two tones, one in his left ear, the other in his right. It sounded like a flute. He smelled a beautiful fragrance in the air, which had taken on a purple hue to it, as if the atmosphere had become a newly blossomed lilac.

He was brimming with anticipation but still the guide with the final teaching did not appear. His thoughts took over again. Have they forgotten about me here? He wondered how many earth days had elapsed during his stay here. There was no sun in this place, only a bright all-encompassing light the color of which seemed to change depending on the context of the learning that occurred. Having no days and nights didn't allow for time measurement, therefore, no real time existed here. He felt very strange, as he sensed uncertainty sweeping over him. The more he focused on his uncertainty, the quicker it turned into fear. His palms got clammy, and his heart began to race as his anxiety quickly grew. He felt dizzy and was sick to his stomach. He couldn't believe this could be happening to him in the Spirit World!

The wind was now blowing hard in his face and the music had become very dissonant. The wind rolled the red stone right up to the base of his feet, as it was almost perfectly round.

As he felt almost like vomiting, he picked it up and instantly Teaching One flashed across the screen of his consciousness. It was like a voice in his brain. "Know the difference between right and wrong. Right ends suffering, wrong creates suffering."

He spoke out loud. "I'm suffering because I'm not using the teachings!" It was a revelation, and instantly the pain began to subside.

He picked up the orange stone. In his mind he heard, "Fear is the enemy, Love is the cure." He realized he had allowed fear to completely overtake him. He chose a loving thought - his mother. He visualized his mother smiling at him. He smiled back, and all pain was immediately gone.

He took notice that the moment the feeling of love had swept over him, all fear and pain were gone.

He was thankful, but still, wondered about Teaching Seven.

Then he had an idea. He picked up the purple stone. He breathed deeply, returning to his meditative state. He felt confidence and peace vibrate throughout his body. He held the purple stone in his right hand, and as he started singing, brought the stone up to his heart.

The scope of his vision erupted in a purple explosion that kept becoming lighter and lighter. The purple was turning into radiant white light, pure as brilliant sunlight but not blinding for his eyes to behold. Soon, all was brilliant white, save for purple ancient symbols the likes of which he had never seen, hovering in mid--air directly before him.

Though he'd never seen them, he could decipher their
meaning, and they said, Surrender and Detach for All is on
schedule. He smiled and nodded, as the symbols slowly
dissipated. A myriad of unknown instruments played the
most beautiful music he could possibly comprehend. Out of
the brilliant whiteness came smiling, singing people, some
holding hands, some reaching lovingly towards him with
outstretched arms. There were people with very light skin,
people with light brown skin like his, people with very dark,
rich, beautiful skin, others had a golden-yellow shade to
their skin, some red, others even blue and green. They
were all singing the same song. He had heard it before. It
had no words, only intricate rhythmic twists and lovely
harmonies that in his soul said, "You are safe, for you are
home, and we are all one."

He knew these were his ancestors, and they kept
coming from the light, and behind them were the four-
legged, and the winged and finned creatures as well. The
creatures sang also, though it was a different song. When
they sang their song over the song of the people, though it
was different, it was perfectly harmonious.

He began singing with them, and tears streamed
down his face. He looked around as he sang, and felt like
he was in the center of an enormous bowl-shaped place
where the people and creatures formed a circle around him.
As people formed a row in front, others behind were
slightly elevated. This continued for as far as he could see,
and he had never felt such joy and unity.

He closed his eyes and felt a deep sense of gratitude.
The singing started to subside, and he became silent. His
eyes were still closed, and he sensed he was alone again.
Then he heard one voice sing again, and opening his eyes,

he saw the beautiful smiling man again, the one who gave him the first teaching.

"Hello again, my son," said the man.

"Father? ... Father!" said White Buffalo, as he leaped to embrace his father.

They embraced for a long time, and it was a sacred Mahamilana, a great union.

"I am so proud of you, my son, you've done well. You now know, the teaching from the Center can only come from within, as that is where Center is. It cannot be given, it must be found. This last teaching lies dormant in all beings. Exposure to, then learning, and finally experiencing the first six teachings opens the doorway to the seventh. The seventh is simple, but not easy to implement. When one evolves to the degree of knowing that all is on schedule, he can surrender to divine will, and adopt detachment as a way of life. Being detached is actually the ultimate way of caring for another. It allows your love for that person to be unpolluted by your personal desires, ensuring that you act for the highest good of all concerned."

"Knowing this concept, it is still a challenge to live it, but immensely rewarding. As an example, I had to apply this with you. It was very difficult to not reveal who I was upon our first meeting here. I knew that having you realize who I was would have distracted you, making you unavailable to the level of comprehension required to glean the Teachings."

"Knowing this, I surrendered to the highest good for all concerned. Trusting Great Spirit as I do, I detached myself, knowing that we would be reunited at the *perfect* time," revealed the boy's father.

"I do understand, father, and I am honored to descend from one so divine," said White Buffalo as he hugged his father again.

"Why did you have to leave earth before I was born?" asked the boy with anguish.

"Prior to my previous incarnation, I had chosen to be a medicine man for our people, to help them prepare for the introduction of the teachings. Once I incarnated, I became distracted by the ways of man, though I always had a secret love of metaphysical things. I hid my interest in these divine ways, believing that my friends would perceive me as strange and weak. Instead, I took up the bow and the horse, trying to convince myself that the deep longing inside myself was foolishness. Then, two months prior to your birth, I volunteered to go on a mission with the chief at the time - Laughing Wolf. Had I listened to the voice within, which whispered my true path, I would not have been where I eventually lost my life. Laughing Wolf and I were ambushed by a war party from the South, and you know the rest. But even this was divine order, because when I left earth, you chose to come to fulfill the ancient prophecy. You are the one, my son, and we love you with all our souls."

At that moment, the purpose of his entire life crystallized. The boy understood his mission, and everything else made perfect sense. Intuitively, he knew it was time to return to Earth. But the longing to stay with his father was so great, he resisted leaving. The Father understood.

"My Father, we are only just united. Ask Great Spirit to allow us a few days together, for I know there is much wisdom you could share with me that I need to learn to better serve our people.

"Dear Son, were I to be selfish, I would have you stay here with me. Yet, as you well know, your place is to return to Earth and share the light of knowledge with our family there. Without the teachings and your guidance for their implementation, The People are in serious danger of extinction. Now is the time, and you are ready. Staying any longer will only make your departure more difficult, so you must go now," said his father, somewhat sadly.

"Every second of the remainder of your life on Earth, I shall protect and guide you as I have done all along. No one could be prouder of you than I, my son," and the beautiful man held his boy for a long time with loving thanks to the Great Spirit.

"One last thing," said the father.

He kissed the boy on both cheeks, then the forehead. "Give this to your mother for me, she'll know what it means ..." White Buffalo saw a flash of light turn into a silver cord. He looked at his father who was effortlessly moving away from him, as he was waving good-bye. The boy reluctantly slid down the silver cord, accompanied by the rushing sound once again. The musical note was there again sounding louder and louder until it became deafening. Then his body began to ache and he saw a sudden flash.

4
LIFE OR DEATH?

Great Bear sadly smudged the black paint on his face and chest. Crystal Eagle Woman had left moments before, imploring him to help her prepare the way for White Buffalo to enter the world of their ancestors. Three days before, she had felt her son squeeze her hand, and was sure he would regain consciousness. Sadly, he did not, and seemed to drift off deeper into his comatose state. She had a faraway look in her eyes, like that of a lost child. White Buffalo was dying, and she had begun to surrender herself to that fact. What no one knew was her plan to climb the Mountain of the Broken Rock, and hurl herself into the gorge. She believed that wherever her husband and son were would be Spirit World to her, and she decided after her son died, she would join them.

Wolf with a Heart and Stone Hawk silently entered Great Bear's tent. Stone Hawk was fighting back tears, as he had felt tremendous guilt over the past seven days for having goaded White Buffalo beyond his ability to safely navigate the steep mountain, and now he was moments from death.

The changes in Stone Hawk over the past week were far-reaching and complex. The once loud-mouthed, slow-witted bully had been acting quietly, thoughtfully and obediently. His parents actually appreciated the fate that had befallen White Buffalo, for their son was now better behaved. They thought only of how things directly affected them, with little compassion for the feelings of others.

Stone Hawk had silently made a blood vow to himself and his ancestors to continue the work that White Buffalo had begun, and over the past week had acted the way he thought his dying friend would. The guilt-ridden boy was changed forever, and determined to become an honorable man.

Wolf with a Heart felt sad and helpless, much as he had the day, thirteen years before, when he had found his father's mutilated and lifeless body, killed by the Mocktaw tribe from the south. The Mocktaws had a signature way of killing their enemies, severing the hands and feet in a way that didn't kill the tortured victim, then eventually beheading them to end their life. The fear this warlike tribe struck into the hearts of the other four nations was legendary, but Wolf with a Heart hated them too much to be afraid.

His father had been the chief, and that they dared to treat his people with such disrespect sparked an intense flame of hatred within him. The great canyon that separated their tribes had acted as a buffer for many moons, but shortly before his father's death, several Mocktaw war parties had been seen in their country. The great canyon was so difficult to cross, the elders never believed a war would happen between the tribes. He had found his father's remains far from the village, but they never found White Buffalo's father's body, which probably was thrown into the depths of the great canyon.

After sending his father's body to the next world in a funeral pyre, Wolf with a Heart set about the task of preventing a war, and exacting his own revenge. He believed the elders of his tribe would raid the Mocktaw Country to restore honor to their people by killing as many braves as they could, possibly even the chief, Fierce Calf. This chief had five sons, and a very powerful medicine man named Crazy Eyes. Stories of his black magic were known to the five nations, and no tribe wished to incur his wrath. Wolf with a Heart decided this war would take a terrible toll on his own people and, that if he could kill either Fierce Calf, Crazy Eyes, or any of the five sons, this would avenge his father's death, restoring respect to his people and saving many of their own lives. All the five tribes lived by the law 'an eye for an eye'. Because of this law, he believed he had the right to kill only one of their leaders as revenge for his father's death. Two Shantee braves had been killed by the Mocktaws, but only his father's body had been found. Killing more than one Mocktaw would incite a war, not prevent it.

Wolf with a Heart and his best friend, Standing Tree, secretly set out on their mission. They headed off in the direction that his father's body had been discovered. After riding for two days to that spot, they spent the night contemplating their next move. At sunrise, they rode on for another day and then another. He began to get discouraged, but that night his father's face appeared in a dream, saying nothing, only smiling and pointing towards the setting sun. This was the direction in which they had been traveling and Wolf with a Heart took this as a sign to continue on that path.

Late afternoon of the next day, they reached a point where the canyon walls came closer together than any other place they had ever seen or heard of. Between these points of land extended a rim jutting up off of the canyon floor below. The rim was about an arrow's length wide and would be very dangerous to traverse, but they believed this was the way that the Mocktaws had entered their country, and they would do the same. Since the Shantee were peaceful people, they had honored the Mocktaws by never entering their country, so Wolf with a Heart had no idea where the village would be, but he felt guided in his mission and slept well that night.

Just before sunrise, Standing Tree nudged his friend awake, and they heard voices on the other side of the canyon. The two Shantee braves stayed still and silent for hours until the Mocktaw party moved on as it began to lightly rain. Though they were wet, they felt energized, for they realized that they could follow the riders' tracks in the mud directly back to their village.

The only way to navigate onto the rim across the canyon was to get off the ponies and to carefully walk them to the other side. Their fear was one of complete exposure and vulnerability if discovered during the crossing, and of the ponies getting spooked or falling into the precipice taking the men with them.

They crossed the rim to the other side uneventfully and picked up the tracks that they hoped would lead to the village. The Mocktaw party totaled five riders in all, and the two Shantee figured they were about an hour behind them. They rode on into the late afternoon as the rain stopped. The scenery was magnificent with high buttes protruding like reddish brown fingers into the sky, and majestic mountains off in the distance surrounding the mesa they rode upon. Just before sunset, they saw that the tracks led up to a gentle mountain. Both Wolf with a Heart and Standing Tree tied their ponies to a cactus and ascended the mountain on foot.

Reaching the top, they carefully peeked over the other side as a panoramic vista unfolded before them. There were hundreds and hundreds of tepees painted differently to signify the individual stories and histories of the families that lived in them. There were many long sticks extending from the ground with twenty to thirty ponies tied to each of them. There were trees cut down and formed into gallows on which hung buffalo and deer meat as it dried in the sun. Women were busy harvesting corn, sage, tomatoes and other herbs and crops.

Suddenly, Wolf with a Heart had an idea and he motioned for Standing Tree to follow him. They quietly and carefully went back down the small mountain, took the ponies and sought an out-of-the-way crevice in the wall of the mountain to spend the night and plan.

They had to ride for hours to find the right place, but

they did, and on the way found a small indentation in the rock that contained rain water for the ponies and themselves to drink. They rested and ate dried buffalo meat as they formulated their plan.

"The Harvest Moon grows full," said Wolf with a Heart. "Seeing the women harvesting corn reminded me of our own harvest festival. They are sure to have their celebration soon to thank the Great Spirit for food, sun, air, and rain. When they dance at night, we will sneak in and try to kill one of their leaders."

"How do we know when this will happen?", asked Standing Tree.

"When the moon is fat, the festival will begin, either tomorrow or the next day. We must be patient and wait," said Wolf with a Heart resolutely.

The next day it rained and the skies were cloudy. It was hard to be still as time passed slowly. The moon was hidden by the clouds, and they could do nothing but wait patiently.

The following day was clear and bright, and as the sun set, the Shantee braves made their way up the mountain, leaving the ponies tied off nearby in case a hasty exit was required.

The moon was large and round, but the flame from the huge fire created so much smoke and light that it dimmed the lunar brightness.

Thousands of people were dancing and singing, but there was an edge to the proceedings. These people were harder, and more quick to be violent, than were the Shantee. The women rarely looked the men in the eye, and the children were treated as pets by the hierarchy, which was dominated by men.

Wolf with a Heart and Standing Tree took half the night moving inches at a time, trying to slowly work their way close enough to get off an arrow at one of the leaders. Once, Standing Tree was almost discovered by a child who strayed far from the fire, and Wolf with a Heart remembered how his friend had earned his name. Standing Tree stayed in one position, motionless, for an incredibly long time, until he was sure it was safe and Wolf with a Heart marveled at him. He would hate to see his good friend die this night, but they had both resigned themselves to die if need be.

As the dancers whooped and gyrated around the fire, they would pass the largest tepee and pay special homage to two figures sitting on a blanket surrounded by five young warriors.

Wolf with a Heart watched them for hours and occasionally someone would accidentally dance too close to the man with the largest headdress, and one of the surrounding braves would smash the offender to the ground. Wolf with a Heart was wondering how he would get off a clean shot, when suddenly a woman approached the chief and his sons. She was very beautiful and bowed low and they all began talking. Suddenly, two of the sons began yelling and gesturing harshly at each other, as if they were arguing over what she had said, or possibly over her. The chief seemed to get angry and stood up. Wolf with a Heart felt the 'now or never' sensation within and, jumping to his feet, drew an arrow to his bow. As he pulled the bowstring back, he saw an arrow whiz by the old man's head.

Standing Tree had just missed! Few of the dancers even
noticed, but the sons and surrounding warriors did. At that
moment, Wolf with a Heart exhaled slightly and aimed six
inches over the chief's head, allowing for drop in the flight
of the arrow over the long distance. He let the arrow fly,
and as the sons looked off in the direction of Standing Tree,
no one saw the arrow slam into the forehead of the chief,
killing him instantly.

Because of the ensuing confusion, the two Shantee
braves were able to get a good head start down the
mountain. The first arrow came from one direction, the kill
shot came from another, and with the chief dead, no one
took command until Crazy Eyes dispatched the sons to take
two war parties and go in both directions. By that time,
Standing Tree and Wolf with a Heart had been able to re-
unite at the summit, and they both slid down the side of the
mountain quickly on the loose scree. This was highly
dangerous as their momentum became so great that if either
of them lost his balance, he would tumble the rest of the
way down the mountain. This would surely mean death,
either from the fall, or from the inability of the injured man
to ride and escape. Crouching low, with one foot in front
of the other, their hands lightly touched the ground on either
side of them, steadying their balance point as they surfed
down the mountain on the loose rock.

Both arrived safely at the bottom, and they sprinted
to their ponies with no pursuer in sight. They raced off into
the night and didn't stop riding hard until they reached the
canyon.

They made it home safely and, for the ensuing
thirteen years, an uneasy truce remained in place between

the Shantee and the Mocktaw.

Wolf with a Heart had been named chief for his heroic deed, and it was only months later that he had spotted the White Buffalo storming through the woods. He would never forget that day, for as he had excitedly hurried back to the village to share his vision with the people, Crystal Eagle Woman was entering the other end of the village with her new baby. And now, Wolf with a Heart was going to have to perform the death dance for this boy, and his heart was heavy.

Great Bear, Stone Hawk, and their chief were all wearing the death paint as they somberly walked to the tepee where White Buffalo lay dying.

They walked into the tent, and saw Crystal Eagle Woman kneeling next to her son, singing a death song which went:

> In a holy way I am talking
> On a ray of light he is walking
> With his father back to you, Great Spirit
> On a ray of light he is bringing
> In a holy way he is singing
> With his father
> Back to you, Great Spirit

Stone Hawk began crying, and Great Bear gently reached out to console him, but was stopped by Wolf with a Heart.

The chief grabbed the boy and shook him. "Do not dishonor the dying with your weakness! We must bravely send him to his ancestors!" chastised the chief. Just then White Buffalo's body convulsed and he began coughing.

His mother was hugging him, and he opened his eyes and was trying to speak.

The chief and his mother knelt down next to him as he whispered, "My hand ... make tea ..." then collapsed from the effort.

His fists were clenched tightly, and his mother pried one hand open and seven colored stones rolled onto the floor of the tepee.

"What is this?" she wondered aloud, as each person in the tent picked up one of the stones with the strange markings. Wolf with a Heart then opened the dying boy's other hand and shouted "Look!" In his hand White Buffalo held a strange purple flower with a yellow center, and the center was glowing!

"I've never seen anything like it," said Great Bear, the elder.

Crystal Eagle Woman thought for a few seconds, then ran from the dwelling, only to return a moment later with a vessel filled with water. She put three petals of the flower in the water and placed it on the fire.

In a short time the water became violet-colored as the petals began to dissolve, becoming tea. She poured a cupful, let it cool, then forced her son to sit up and drink some of the herbal mixture. White Buffalo's eyes bulged slightly, and he began coughing and shuddering.

"It's killing him," gasped Stone Hawk with fear.

"Silence, boy!!" yelled the chief.

This same procedure was repeated over and over as the sun set, and then deep into the night. They all stood vigil over the fallen boy, and by morning, Great Bear and

Stone Hawk were sleeping, but Crystal Eagle Woman and Wolf with a Heart had remained awake all night long.

The mother nudged the elder and the sleeping boy, and as they awoke, they looked up to see White Buffalo sitting up, looking groggy, but managing a faint smile.

He whispered weakly to his mother, "I have something for you from someone who misses you dearly. He leaned over and kissed both her cheeks and forehead.

She put her hand to her mouth which was agape, but no words could come out. When her husband had been gone on a hunt or a mission, this was his special way of greeting her, of telling her how much he loved and missed her.

The implications were staggering - where was her son for the last seven days? Obviously, he must have been with his father.

She looked at her son, "How did you know of this?" she asked in astonishment.

"Father told me to give this to you, mother. But I am weary. I need rest, then I will reveal all, for I have much to share," and the boy fell back into a deep sleep.

5
THE LEARNING CIRCLES

Though he denied possession of any special powers regarding his miraculous recovery, White Buffalo was now looked upon by The People as a medicine man closer to the Great Spirit than any other.

When he had fully recovered, he explained to the council of elders, and everyone else who would sincerely listen, about his journey to the land of their ancestors.

He taught The People about The Teachings and their symbols, and implored them to apply this wisdom in their everyday lives. The evidence of the stones, and the healing flower, made his story irrefutable. The purple healing flower had twelve petals, three of which his mother had used to heal him. He used the other nine so discerningly, he was able to stretch their healing powers out over the course of nine years.

He was now 21 years old, and he had grown to be a beautiful man, inside and out.

Though he was physically handsome, it was his inner peace and joy that made people desire his company. He was never too busy to counsel anyone, regardless of their status in the tribe. He was becoming a living example of the Teachings. He decided to hold daily learning circles so the children could be exposed to the Teachings at an early age, because many of the adults nodded wisely, but continued to act in the old ways.

The children began to react in ways that shocked their parents, for they trusted in White Buffalo so completely that they implemented the lessons of the teachings in every facet of their daily lives and they began teaching the parents!

Soon, the parents started to attend the learning circles, which began each morning after breakfast. White Buffalo would begin the learning circle with a song or toning together. At first, everyone would be singing their own individual note, but after a few minutes the group would all be singing the same note, which seemed to bring the group together as one.

Then White Buffalo would chant a spontaneous prayer which included an acknowledgment of the intent of the circle. "Dear Great Spirit, We honor you who gave life and love to all things. We honor our ancestors for giving life to our parents and for guiding us always from the spirit world. We honor our parents for giving us our lives and for feeding and teaching us to the best of their abilities."

"We come together to learn and share teachings of a sacred manner, to gently shift the vibrations of our world from a predominantly fearful state to one of love."

"With your love, all things are possible. We ask for you to shine your light of knowledge into the darkness of our ignorance. Thank you, Great Spirit. And so it is!" White Buffalo would say something similar to this each time and would end his opening prayer with hands together in a praying mode, looking beseechingly toward the heavens.

Then the sharings would begin. Discussions ensued as to how the Teachings were used to better a situation, or how they could have been used, but weren't. When the group reached an impasse, their medicine man would always have the appropriate words and actions to guide the energy towards love and learning.

"What is Teaching Two, Singing Bird?" asked White Buffalo of a ten-year-old boy.

"Fear is the enemy, love is the cure."

"Excellent, my son, and did anything happen this week to enable you to live this Teaching?" said the teacher.

"Well, I think so," the child replied bashfully.

"When the thunder and lighting came yesterday, my sister became afraid as she usually does, and hid under the blankets in our tent."

"So when I asked her what was wrong, she said that she was afraid of the thunder, lightning, and the wind."

"What did you tell her?" asked White Buffalo.

"I told her that I understand why she's scared and I used to be scared of the thunder and the wind, too. Then I told her that when the thunder beings brought the rain, a thunder clap was how they warned us to go inside and not be caught in the rain. And that every time it rained, it was Great Spirit's way of saying how much he loved us and wanted to make our plants grow, so we could eat and drink clear water. Without rain, we would die, and without thunder, we'd be caught in the rain and be cold."

White Buffalo was nodding and smiling with approval as the boy continued.

"I told my sister that the thunder had to be loud so no matter where we were, we could hear it. Great Spirit does this because he loves us so much, so don't be afraid. And when I said that, she smiled and hugged me!" said the boy proudly.

Singing Bird's mother wrapped both arms around her son's shoulders, lovingly amazed at his wisdom. But Singing Bird's father, who was having problems accepting and understanding the Teachings, stood up with a pained expression and said, "I think fear is good and wise. You cannot love everything, for there is much danger out there! If this child tries to love a bear, the bear will kill him!"

The words were said in an attacking manner, but White Buffalo understood that it was just the man's nature which made him speak in that way. The father was truly concerned that his son's gentleness would get him killed.

White Buffalo stood and looking tenderly into the father's eyes said, "All creatures of nature communicate with each other through vibrations, not words, as we humans do. When you fear a creature, it senses your fear, which in turn, sets off the fight or run instinct in the creature. If the creature is a squirrel, there is no problem. But if it is a bear, a person could get killed. Your son is living the love principle so powerfully that the bear would feel your boy's love, and would not be threatened. The challenge is not to escape the bear, it is to escape your fear. My friend, does this make sense?" asked the teacher gently.

The father put his hand to his chin and thought for a moment. Then he said, "That may work with an animal, but not with a Mocktaw. If he tried to love a Mocktaw, he'd lose his hands, feet, and head!"

This statement had quite an effect on the group. Then White Buffalo said to the father, "You are wise, sir, and you are a brave hunter. I know you as a good father, also. Your last statement can be answered by applying another Teaching."

The teacher then turned to Singing Bird and said, "Young man, if you saw a Mocktaw warrior, what would you do?" The boy thought for a moment, hesitating only because he didn't want to appear to be smarter than his father. "My father made me promise that if I saw a Mocktaw, I would return to the village immediately and warn the tribe."

"How many other children here think that is the correct answer?" inquired White Buffalo. All of the children in the group raised their hands. "Which Teachings apply to Singing Bird's answer?" asked the teacher. Many hands shot up instantly. The teacher chose a little girl up front.

"Life works to the extent that you keep your word?" she said in an adorably high voice, sounding slightly unsure of herself by answering in the form of a question.

"Little Wing, can you explain how this Teaching fits the situation?" The whole group turned to look at her, as some of the other children started to giggle, making her feel self-conscious and she shook her head no. The medicine man held up his hands and said sternly, "Silence people." The group obeyed the teacher, who said "Please, Little Wing, tell us your thoughts." She wrung her hands together, moving her shoulders back and forth as she chose her words thoughtfully. "Singing Bird promised his daddy to warn the village, and if he didn't, that would be lying," she said sweetly.

"Yes, my child, very good!" said White Buffalo emphatically while stroking the top of her head. "Would any other Teaching apply?" he asked of the group.

"Do what has to be done, when it has to be done." It was Singing Bird's father. The teacher smiled admiringly as he walked over, putting his hand on the man's shoulder to silently thank him for his valuable contributions to the day's lessons.

"By keeping his word to his father, Singing Bird immediately does what has to be done, and returns to the village to warn his people!" said the teacher proudly as he summed up the story. All we're trying to do in these learning circles is live in a way that allows everyone the chance to feel fulfillment and happiness, for that is the Great Spirit's wish for us, his children."

"The main ingredient to achieve happiness in life is to have inner peace. Without inner peace, there is no joy in life. To obtain inner peace, one must learn to live a balanced, harmonious existence. Balance is the key to achieving inner peace. These teachings outline a way for us to live in a balanced, centered fashion. Once we attain balance, we become transformed by peace on the inside and the outside."

As White Buffalo said this, he was watching the reaction of the people, and he could sense that he had lost many of them.

"Happiness in life has nothing to do with the beauty of your tepee or how many ponies you have!" he said, raising his voice. "Great Bear, would you tell the story about Rides like the Wind?" he asked of the wise elder. Great Bear was the oldest living member of the Shantee people. He did not speak much, but when he did, his words had tremendous value. White Buffalo always looked up to him, and on the rare occasion when he could not get his message across to the people, he would ask the elder for help.

Great Bear thought in silence for a few minutes. Just as the children began to get restless, he spoke. "My grandfather's name was Great Bear, as was my father's and now I have the name. My grandfather's friend was named 'Rides Like the Wind'. He was a great rider, and he and the other braves liked to race their ponies. They would bet their ponies on who would win the race, and Rides Like the Wind soon owned a large herd of the fastest ponies. Many young women were impressed by this, and they fought over who would become his squaw, and eventually, he married the prettiest girl in our village. Whenever they needed anything, he would trade some ponies for it. He and his wife had many children, and soon they had the biggest tepee in the village."

"Now, back then, our ancestors lived on the same side of the Great Canyon as the Mocktaw. They were more peaceful then, but were beginning to grow warlike. My grandfather said that they started to have skirmishes with our people during hunts far from the village, but as time went by, they became braver and more aggressive. Then one day they attacked our village. They attacked just before sunrise, and because our braves were sleeping, they just rode in and began killing people." The old man's voice became sad as he continued his grandfather's story. "Most people just ran out of their tents with their families, jumped on their ponies and rode away. But Rides Like the Wind could not bring himself to leave his ponies. He had connected his sense of self-worth to his ponies, and believed somewhere inside him that without them, he wouldn't be respected. So he was trying to leave with all his ponies, and the Mocktaws killed him and his eldest son, and stole their ponies anyway." The old man fell silent.

White Buffalo had sat down so as to give Great Bear center stage attention, and after the elder finished, he stood up and again addressed the group.

"Rides Like the Wind believed that possessions created greatness in his life, but in reality, his possessions created his death."

"Thank you, Great Bear. Your wisdom has taken us where I could not lead. Now my friends, what Teaching, had he learned it, could have saved Rides Like the Wind?"

A hand went up in the very back of the circle. It was White Buffalo's best friend, Stone Hawk. The muscular brave said, "Surrender and detach, for all is on schedule."

"Stone Hawk, how does this Teaching apply here?"

"Surrendering is not giving up, it speaks to knowing how to act for the good of the whole. If Rides Like the Wind had been able to detach from owning his ponies, he and most importantly his son, would have lived to fight another day."

"And how could being attacked by the Mocktaws be termed, All is on schedule?" asked White Buffalo.

"The ways of the Great Spirit are mysterious and reach deeply to affect the generations. Wisdom and learning are often the offspring of disastrous events. When we were boys, I conceitedly pushed you into danger, and your near-death experience has transformed our whole way of life!" said Stone Hawk with eloquence.

Side by side with White Buffalo, Stone Hawk had become a living example of how these Teachings could create happiness and success in life. He was an honored brave, teacher, and the father of Little Wing.

"Your words are wise and true, my brother, thank you," said the teacher to his best friend. "The circle is complete this morning, but before we go about our work today, I want to leave you with a thought," and the teacher stopped to choose his words carefully. "The Teaching from the West is to be someone who positively influences all life forms. I want to embellish on this today. Living in harmony and balance with nature shows great reverence and respect. Nature understands our efforts to respect her, and then makes her powers available to us. In other words, the more respect we show nature, and all of her life forms, the more power we are given and the more she will listen to our prayers for rain, sun, mild winters, or anything we need from her," said White Buffalo slowly and cautiously.

"Are you telling us that we can control the weather?" asked Wolf with a Heart with astonishment in his voice. The Chief rarely spoke at the learning circles, but everyone in the tribe knew how much he respected White Buffalo's work, and that the medicine man's advice was valued greatly by the chief.

"I am saying you are more powerful than any of you currently know, except possibly the little ones. They haven't been taught what they can't do yet. When you live the Teachings every day, your life balances, which in turn awakens dormant regions of your mind which everyone possesses but rarely learns to use. These places are where the Great Spirit exists in us, and accessing these realms connects us with the mind of The Great Spirit. When we are connected to the mind of The Great Spirit, we do not control the weather, we BECOME the weather. We cannot truly control anything but our own thoughts and actions. Living the Teachings creates constant love, understanding, and balance, which is the key to open up the doorway in your mind that connects to the mind of the Great Spirit. Without love and understanding, it is impossible to do, which is how Great Spirit protects this power from falling into the hands of evil-doers."

"I know these concepts are new to you, and they can be difficult to grasp, but you are ready, my people. Think about it. We are his children, therefore, we must carry the parent's seed within us, as do all children. But the only way to connect to him is by fully becoming what he is, which is - LOVE."

"I first spoke of this concept at the end of last summer after the drought. Now it is spring, and we need good rains this summer. I am teaching a new way to ensure a bountiful crop this year. Link up with the mind of Great

Spirit within and all things are possible. Now, go in peace," and he sat down, silent at last.

6
THE UNITY PLAN

White Buffalo had been spending much of his time alone in nature, meditating on how to re-unite the five nations. The relationship he had developed with his father during his visit to the spirit world had continued to exist though White Buffalo was back on earth. He communicated with his father during sessions that he called "Sacred Sitting". He would sit quietly and just breath, emptying all thoughts from his mind. When Stone Hawk asked why this was important, the teacher replied, "Without space in the tepee, there is no room to live. Without space in your thoughts, there is no room to expand your awareness. "Sacred Sitting" creates space between our thought patterns, turning off the normal day-to-day sensors. When normal mental limitations are suspended, extraordinary things can happen."

Stone Hawk and several others, many of whom were women and children, belonged to a special group of advanced students of the Teachings. The teacher called this group the "holders of the sacred vision". He taught them "Sacred Sitting" and some had even developed the ability to talk with their ancestors, as did their teacher. It always began the same way - deep breathing leading to a place of total peace and awareness.

White Buffalo would then see colors in his mind's eye, swirling colors that would begin to take shape. Eventually, the face of his father, smiling and peaceful, would appear in the center of his mind. He would ask questions of his father and tell him about Crystal Eagle Woman. Once he even contacted Laughing Wolf, whom he let speak through his body to his son, Wolf with a Heart. When Laughing Wolf, speaking through White Buffalo, reminded Wolf with a Heart of their first buffalo hunt together, how the young boy had fallen off his horse, face down in the mud, Wolf with a Heart's eyes grew wide. The father had never told anyone of his son's embarrassing fall, only of their victory in bringing meat home on his son's first hunt. It was a secret kept between a son and a father, one they would laugh about together on other hunts even years later.

The chief started laughing, and then the laughter died down, and he began crying. Wolf with a Heart was very uncomfortable with this, but he could not help it, he missed his father so. And now, here he was, speaking through his friend!

"It is good to cry, my son," his father said in White Buffalo's voice.

"One cannot hold in all the emotions of life, only to explode on some unsuspecting victim. Though I miss you, I'm very fulfilled and happy here. I had to leave earth for you to become who you are for our people. You are a better chief than I could have been. In my earth body, I could not have accepted the Teachings that White Buffalo has used to awaken our people to their true selves. Great Spirit in his infinite wisdom knew this, and so the divine plan marched on. The seeds of our destiny are planted through our own actions. The law of cause and effect was built into our existence by the Great Spirit at the beginning of creation long, long ago. He does not meddle in our day to day affairs. Our actions spontaneously determine what happens to us. I had a very important role as the leader of our tribe. As such, it was imperative that I connect with my spiritual self to be able to make better decisions for the good of our people. My ego (the false self) would not allow me to do so. This was my own decision, and it, added together with many other bad choices, led to my death."

"You and White Buffalo are leading our people wisely, you are fulfilling your destiny, and are honoring your ancestors and your descendants. We are always watching. Go in Peace," and White Buffalo's voice fell silent.

Wolf with a Heart wiped away his tears, and he could see that White Buffalo was still deep in contemplation. White Buffalo's father was speaking to him.

"Ancestors from the Mocktaws are close friends of mine in this world. They have come recently to tell me that their children in your world are suffering and planning to war. The time to unite is drawing near my son, you will see. Choose wisely, and know that our help is always here for you. Goodbye for now," and his father was gone.

The next day in the learning circle, the whole village attended. They sang together, and the song was so harmonious, White Buffalo could feel the power and balance of his people, and he was proud. He said the prayer and then spoke of the day's agenda.

"Today, we begin to work with mother nature to unite our energies, and those of the five nations. It is time to plant our seeds in the earth. This year, when we plant, bless each seed to grow to its fullest potential so as to feed the world. As you put the seed into the ground, do so with love in your heart, for believe me, the seed can feel it! As you pat the earth down over the seed, promise it that you will honor it and nurture it."

Once you have done this, we will pray to the Earth spirits for the perfect balance of rain, sun, and wind. We will do this each day, and we will sing to the crops each day also, and our harmonious vibrations will help create a harvest like none that has ever been reaped.

The father of Singing Bird stood up, eager to speak. "Game has been plentiful, and though we had a drought last year, our stores of corn lasted the winter. I have seen many new fields which we are intending to seed, ten times more than our nation could eat, or store for the winter. Why are we doing this?" he asked, with a puzzled expression.

"Last summer, we sent messengers to confer with the chiefs of all other nations, except the Mocktaws. We invited the other nations to our harvest festival, asking the

leaders, teachers, and grandfathers of each nation to attend.
We also asked for the brightest women and children from
each nation to come, and to bring empty wagons with them.
We asked them to be guests in our nation for one full phase
of the moon.", said White Buffalo, nodding to the chief.

Wolf with a Heart stood up and continued speaking.
"We intend to share the Teachings with the brightest and
best from each nation. They will be part of our learning
circles, and hopefully take the knowledge and the stones
back to their nation. We plan on sending them back with
wagons full of corn, squash, beans and buffalo meat," said
their chief. All of our people must see that they are
respected and loved by their cousins across the great plain.
Our ancestors have prepared the way, and now is the time
to help better the lives of all people in this world. Talking
is one thing, but feeding them will prove our truth and
power. They will know our sincerity through our actions.
Our relatives will hear the truth from the children, they will
feel the unity of our learning circles, and they will take food
home to fill the bellies of their people. In this way, we will
begin to make the Teachings known to all," the chief
concluded, looking back at White Buffalo.

Stone Hawk stood and said, "What about the
Mocktaws, are they to be invited?"

"Yes, Stone Hawk, the Mocktaws are also our
cousins, and they must be invited," said the teacher. "You
and I must go to their main village with gifts to show our
intent. We must, at all cost, try to convey our genuine
desire for peace and cooperation. Great Spirit is most
needed by those who are yet to understand his ways, and the
Mocktaws truly need the teachings, though they are

probably unaware of how imperative this meeting is to their survival."

"The Mocktaws are savages! They don't deserve our friendship or our food, all they deserve is our spears and arrows!" A young brave, Fighting Calf, stood angrily, fists clenched, and continued. "They don't look like us, they don't act like us, and have shown only hatred for us!"

White Buffalo shook his head. "No, Fighting Calf, they are children of the Great Spirit, the same as you and I ..."

"No! No!" shouted the young brave. "I will not hear this! I believe in the Teachings, but these people killed your father and our former chief. They are not children of the Great Spirit, they are cast-offs of our race who must be exiled, or eliminated!"

Great Bear, the grandfather, stood with his arms held out. Without speaking, the simple motion of this old man created silence among the group. Fighting Calf reluctantly sat down, his face still flushed with anger. "It is time to heal all wounds. Our nations stand divided, but it is a new era. We must not divide, we must multiply. Fighting Calf speaks the truth of a young man, I speak the truth of the elders. Neither is wrong, but peace is right! His way is not peaceful, and it is a time for unity of all. Imagine life in the highest sense - respect for all living things, giving food to those in need, sharing the Teachings with all people. The duty of having knowledge is to share it, not horde it. Sharing knowledge is a major step towards living knowledge which is when it becomes wisdom. We need your help my young warrior, so as to unite in spirit the purpose of this shift towards unity. Let me be clear about our purpose.

The time has come to act as one force, one heart, one voice singing the same song. The power of such a group is unlimited. Let me tell you a story."

        "When I was a young brave, Fighting Calf's age, a group of wild ponies was discovered, and their leader was an all white pony with red eyes. We named the animal Fire Eyes, and he became the object of desire for all young braves in the village. To capture this magnificent creature would earn that brave great respect among The People. Every young man was out trying to snare Fire Eyes, but for a long time the pony out-smarted us all. Then one day, a group of us were hunting in a ravine near the Mountain of the Broken Rock, when we saw a large dust cloud coming up the ravine. We all hid behind rocks and trees with great anticipation, and sure enough, it was the herd of wild ponies led by Fire Eyes. To my good fortune, the white pony happened to run directly beneath me as I was hiding in a tree, and I jumped on his back. As I did so, my best friend threw a rope around his neck! The pony put up a fight, but there were five of us, and the other braves grabbed his tail, and as we brought him under control, we began fighting over who would get to keep the pony. We were bickering like fools, when Fire Eyes made a last ditch effort to escape our bonds. He reared up on his hind legs, throwing me off, and as he spun around, his front leg came down in the crevice of a huge boulder. His leg was bleeding and stuck, but was not broken. My friend who had lassoed the pony said, 'The brave who can push back the rock to free Fire Eyes will have earned the right to keep him!' We all agreed, and one at a time, we individually tried to push back the boulder. But the rock was massive, and not one of us could budge it. Then, the youngest of us, Laughing Wolf, made a suggestion. He said that the only way to free Fire Eyes was to unite our energy, and that together we would succeed."

"Begrudgingly at first, we all got behind the rock, and it only moved a little. But we were energized by this, and a force came over us. It was as if by getting together, our strength became magnified. Our next heave moved the rock even more, and the pony whinnied. With great shouts of power and strength, we threw ourselves into the boulder a third time, and it rolled off the pony's leg. Fire Eyes scrambled off, limping for a moment, then realizing his leg was not seriously hurt, he sprinted away."

"We were all laughing and cheering, and then Laughing Wolf, who years later would become our chief, said something I will never forget. He said 'We may be powerful alone, but together we are limitless'!"

Great Bear fell silent for a moment, and the people all nodded in approval. He then turned to Fighting Calf and said, "My young brave, we may be powerful alone, but together we are limitless!" As the old man said the word "limitless", White Buffalo closed his eyes and a scene began to unfold in his imagination . . .

* * *

Eons ago, a great king ruled his people with honor and fairness. He ruled the land called Cathay (China) and he and his people lived for many years in happiness until invading hordes of marauders threatened their way of life.

Over the years, the marauding hordes grew in numbers, and they slowly but surely were decimating the countryside and the king's army. The king was filled with anguish as he searched for a solution to their predicament.

He decided to call for a meeting between the leader of the marauders, Mockbar-Khan, and himself. He sent messengers to the Khan, and the meeting time and place were set. They would meet in a city that was equidistant between the capitals of both countries. The king took his royal entourage to the meeting place at the appointed time. The king and his council and guards met with Mockbar-Khan, who was accompanied by his war party.

After polite introductions, Mockbar-Khan asked the king if the two of them could talk privately. The king agreed and they went for a walk in the garden of the palace. The king had decided upon his strategy, which was to offer Mockbar-Khan the huge portion of his kingdom that bordered Khan's country, which for all intents and purposes was already ruled by the Khan, who had conquered it years before, though it did not officially or legally belong to him. When he made his offer, the Khan scoffed at him.

The Khan said, "Your highness wishes to give me that which I already possess? You make me laugh, your majesty, for there is only one way to quench my thirst, and if you do not give me what I want, I shall not stop until I own your palace!" The Khan then glared menacingly right into the king's eyes. The king was completely unafraid, for though he was much older, in his day he had been a great warrior who had long since learned to listen and weigh all options before acting.

"What is it that you want, Khan?" the king calmly

replied.

"I want the hand of your daughter, princess Chantisita, your highness," said Khan, returning back to his phony respectful eloquence.

The king's stomach turned in knots, for he loved his daughter far too much to even think of this. But the more they discussed the situation, the more the king realized that his options were to either give up his kingdom, or his daughter's hand in marriage.

Though Mockbar-Khan was a handsome warrior, he was rough, low-class, and had a darkness about his being. The king hated the idea of his daughter being with Khan, but concluded that the marriage was preferable to his subjects being cruelly governed by Khan and his thugs. He believed that the needs of the many outweighed the wants of the few. The king discussed the situation with Chantisita, and after much thought, she agreed to the marriage.

Mockbar-Khan and Chantisita were married on the next full moon, and they had five sons. Though peace was initially achieved because of the marriage, ten years later, the Khan's war council began to usurp his power. Chantisita saw this coming, and called on her father for help.

"My dear child, my spies in Khan's palace have heard rumors of a possible assassination attempt on your husband. I believe you must take your boys and leave as soon as possible. This month, the wood of the bamboo tree takes on magical qualities. It can remain afloat for one year if it is harvested at the proper time. I will have a sturdy boat built from this bamboo, and you and your five sons can sail towards the rising sun to a new land.

So the king had the boat built, sent twenty hand picked soldiers and sailors to accompany his daughter and her sons, and they sailed east. Shortly after their departure, the Khan's war lords had him assassinated. Despite a very difficult and arduous journey with many men lost at sea, Chantisita and her sons arrived in an uncharted land.

Her five sons grew up to be powerful, strong-willed men. Three of the sons looked like they came from Chantisita's family, having more golden skin, soft black hair, and almond eyes, and the other two sons looked and acted like their father. These two were darker, more warlike, and got along with only each other despite having no memory of their father.

These two sons were named Mocktaw (which means son of Mockbar) and Weekomock (looks like father). The other three sons were named Shantee (which means peaceful one), Mataba (mother's little one), and Savitri (he who shines like the sun). The two sons who were like their father left their mother and brothers, and founded the two nations, the Mocktaws, who favored a war-like behavior, and the Weekamocks, who were also fierce hunters, warriors, and traders.

The other three brothers took loving wives and created the other three nations, The Matabas, the Savitris and the Shantees, and these people were more peaceful, light-hearted, and joyful.

These five tribes lived in the same general area, as each brother initially founded his own village, which eventually became a nation. Mataba, Savitri, and Shantee were so kind and loving as leaders that their people felt the rhythms of happiness and exhibited more love towards each other. Soon many children were born, and the populations grew more rapidly in these three villages than did the populations of Mocktaw and Weekamock. The three villages also maintained stable communications with each other via messengers, smoke signals, and group hunts, while they had little reason to communicate with the other two tribes. Inevitably, the Mocktaws and Weekamocks felt threatened by the large amount of people in the other three nations. They were victims of their own negative beliefs, and ignorance caused them to blame the Shantees, Matabas, and Savitris for their own dwindling populations. Out of paranoia, they hatched a plot to raid the other villages, and steal their secret to happiness. But you cannot steal love and kindness, and the dark ones fell victim to their own hatred.

People began leaving the two warlike tribes to seek a more peaceful environment in which to raise their families, and the other three tribes accepted anyone who was sincerely seeking positive growth. Some of these former Mocktaws warned the three tribes of the impending raid, and the Shantees, Savitris, and Matabas put together a huge army, marched right into the other two nations, and insisted that they move to the other side of the Great Canyon or be vanquished.

The Mocktaws and the Weekamocks reluctantly made the move, and there had been very little contact between them ever since. The Savitris had since moved east across the great mountains to the land of fresh water (the Great Lakes and beyond). The Matabas had moved north to the land of the great plains, and the Shantees had stayed.

Rumor had it among the Shantee people that the Mocktaws and Weekamocks eventually warred, and the

Weekamocks went to the east to the land of the great marsh on the water.

Slowly this great vision of his people's origin began to fade. White Buffalo fell to his knees and laid face down with his arms out-stretched upon the ground in thanks to his ancestors for what he had just witnessed.

With the vision of his people's origin fresh in his mind, the medicine man fully understood the interaction of the tribes with one another.

Later that evening, he called a meeting of the elders to relay all he had learned in the vision. The elders could feel the spirits of their ancestors empowering them to unite the people. They performed the sacred ceremony of the pipe.

White Buffalo filled the red pipestone pipe with bark and sacred herbs, and handed it to Wolf with a Heart, who bowed deeply to honor the power of the pipe. White Buffalo spoke sacred words to honor their ancestors.

> Holy Father and Mother
> We pray for your power.
> Holy sister and brother
> We honor your name.
> All Fathers and Mothers
> Help bring us together.
> All sisters and brothers
> One nation again.

They repeated these words as one voice, and even Fighting Calf spoke the words with sincerity. They passed the pipe and smoked in silence. When it was finished, they meditated together for a long time. Then White Buffalo said, "The symbolic energy of smoking the pipe is like our journey to unite the nations. The herbs and bark are a mixture of five plants and trees which represent the earth spirits of the five nations. I prayed over this mixture, and prepared it in a holy way. Then we "open" the pipe, which means to assign a holy purpose that this pipe is especially used for. This pipe is opened to be used for unity through diversity, and harmony through many voices. Then we say the sacred words, honoring those who prepared the way - our ancestors. After doing this, we put the sacred flame to the pipe, and it represents - OGNAHEE - the fire of knowledge. Then the mixture is transformed from solid to spirit, as the bark becomes smoke. We take our life force energy, our breath, and merge it with the spirit of the symbolic smoke to become one. The power of the earth spirits then unites our life force energy with a divine purpose, which is to live in harmony as one."

The people nodded, for they knew it was very good. They were silent, and after the "Sacred Sitting" one by one, family by family, they went back to their tepees.

Wolf with a Heart smiled and looked at White Buffalo. Their eyes met for a long while, then the medicine man simply said, "And so it begins."

7

THE VEIL IS LIFTED

The Shantees had impeccably followed White Buffalo's instructions on how to create optimum growth for the beans, squash and corn fields, and there had never been such a bountiful crop. Many animals were drawn to feed off of the enormous fields of vegetables, and the braves easily hunted rabbits, foxes, prairie hens and other animals. They gutted and dried the meat in the sun, and in this way, they could preserve the meat without it rotting.

The other three nations, the Matabas, Savitris, and the Weekamocks, sent messengers who graciously acknowledged their intention of attending the festival. All preparations were going as planned. What they could not have known was that the Mocktaws also had a plan that they were executing. They had crossed the Great Canyon with a war party who had been observing the storing of food and game. This war party had returned to their village to tell their medicine man/chief, Crazy Eyes, what they had seen. They reported that the Shantees were preparing huge stores of food to feed a large army. The scouts assumed that the other nations were banding together with the Shantees to slaughter the Mocktaw nation.

Because these scouts thought mainly of war, they inaccurately assumed everyone wanted war, and that is what they reported.

They also had stayed a week in the country of the Shantees, and told Crazy Eyes that it had rained almost every night, and was mostly sunny each day. This enraged the old wizard because on their side of the canyon, the Mocktaws had experienced daily rains which rotted their crops and game was scarce.

Crazy Eyes was darkly powerful, and he believed that the Shantee medicine man had cursed his people by somehow winning the favor of the thunder beings. Because his mind was focused on being deceitful, all he perceived was deceit in other people. His lust for power created a warlike mentality and he consequently convinced himself that others wanted war.

Though they were ruled by an evil wizard, most of the Mocktaws were basically good, simple people. Their greatest character flaw lay in their allowing this tyrant to continue to rule as chief. The hardships the people had to endure were becoming unbearable, and they grew restless. In their unenlightened state, they could not see how they were creating misfortune through negative thinking.

There was an old woman in the Mocktaw tribe whose name was Silver Fox. She had long white hair, and a brown, wrinkled, leather-skinned face, with warm eyes and a quick smile. She was a strong woman with a brilliant mind, and her fairness and wisdom naturally attracted others to seek her counsel. Many years before, she and her husband had been approached by others who wished to overthrow Crazy Eyes. The medicine man had spies who exposed this plan, and all the men involved were killed in the typical Mocktaw fashion, in front of the whole village. Crazy Eyes had these braves tied to stakes driven deep into the ground, and their hands and feet were hacked off with tomahawks. This was not only gruesome torture, but it was meant to teach a lesson to anyone entertaining thoughts of challenging his power. He left them there to bleed for a whole day, then beheaded them. He wasn't sure what to do with Silver Fox, and because he viewed women as inferior creatures, he actually pitied her. He decided to cut out her tongue, and her fate was also carried out in full view of the entire village.

After this happened, people stayed away from her and her one child, a three year old daughter. The woman changed her daughter's name to Words of the Fox, because this girl became the mouthpiece of her mother. Silver Fox would convey her own thoughts through sign language to her daughter, and the girl would speak them. The mother was ostracized because of this incident, and retreated into herself and her daughter. She would go into the woods and mountains and study the animals and nature almost every day for the next twenty years. She had many moments of terrible loneliness which eventually gave way to a quiet acceptance of her circumstances. As the years passed, this quiet acceptance led to a deep connection with the nature spirits, until one day she began to be able to telepathically communicate with the plants and animals. Her telepathy with the plants came as feelings, and with the animals she could actually understand their thoughts as they formed words in her mind.

Once when she was seeking the proper herb to heal her daughter's stomach problems, she went into the forest with the constant thought, "Which one of you can help my child?" projecting from her heart. As she passed many different plants, she felt as if they were sleeping, in this way knowing they could not help her. Deep into the woods, she walked past several bushes that she could hear crying. She didn't actually hear it, but it was the exact same vibration she felt from her daughter when, as an infant, she cried out for attention. The woman sensed these bushes were trying to get her attention, so she lovingly plucked three leaves, and the tea from the leaves quickly cured her daughter.

The relationship Silver Fox had with the animal world was equally powerful. After fifteen years in the forest, she could communicate to every animal, even the insects, though her closest friends were the wolves. There was a large pack of timber wolves that she had a special friendship with, for they were the first "four-legged's" that she learned to communicate with. Silver Fox was in the process of becoming a vegetarian, living off of her knowledge of the forest, as well as the legumes her people grew. She stashed the buffalo meat offered to her, and fed it to the wolves, particularly the huge black wolf she called Blackie. Having lost her ability to speak, her other senses blossomed wildly, and after several years, Blackie became her best friend. He was the size of a small bear, very fierce, and very loyal to his human friend. He eventually became the leader of the pack, which numbered in the hundreds and covered a large portion of Mocktaw country.

For years, Silver Fox was an outcast, viewed as an eccentric forest hermit. But as the Mocktaw people grew more unhappy, her steady wisdom and balanced vibrational state was widely sought after by her fellow villagers.

This infuriated Crazy Eyes, who continued to rule through fear. Every so often, he tried to trap her in a scheme which would allow him to be rid of her, but what he couldn't know, was that she could hear his thoughts. Her telepathic ability allowed her to stay several steps ahead of his schemes.

Silver Fox was quietly being recognized as the unspoken spiritual leader of the Mocktaws. She could sense the growing discontent in the village, and knew why nature was not cooperating with her people. She understood the Law of Vibration which decreed that like attracts like. She realized that nature was mimicking the stifled growth occurring in her tribe with a constant cleansing rain that stifled the growth of their crops. This was Mother Nature's way of cleansing the situation. Her people's negative vibration actually attracted these negative weather patterns to them. Silver Fox could sense the approach of strangers who were good, and she was concerned for their safety. The winds of change were in the air, and she knew a major transformation was coming.

It was decided that White Buffalo, Stone Hawk, and Fighting Calf would go as Shantee peace emissaries whose purpose was to invite the Mocktaws to the harvest festival. They set out on their journey during the moon when the cherries are ripe, and crossed the Great Canyon three days later. Stone Hawk was an excellent tracker, and picked up the trail that he knew would lead to the main Mocktaw village. A hidden Mocktaw scout spotted them, and rode furiously back to the village, reporting the presence of approaching strangers to his chief.

Crazy Eyes rubbed his chin and contemplated what to do. Though his mind was polluted through fear and greed, he still had a quick wit fueled by cunning intelligence. He reasoned that if they wanted to fight, there would be a large band, but only three? What could they be up to? He decided they were either advance scouts probing for weaknesses to later exploit, or a suicide squad whose only mission was to kill him. The old man told his braves to capture the strangers, and bring them directly to him. He added that if they resisted, to kill them.

Though they did not know it, the Shantee peace party was only a couple of hours ride away from the Mocktaw village when they saw a large dust cloud moving nearer to them. The Great Canyon was on the left, and a large plain leading to mountains was on their right side. The war party was now in view, riding hard and fast, red painted faces, screaming and whooping with hatchets held high. It was truly a fearful scene to behold. They were closing the distance between them when White Buffalo spoke.

"My dear brothers, have no fear and do not resist. Remember, fear is the enemy, love is the cure." White Buffalo was smiling with his arms out, palms upward when the first of the twenty-five riders screamed through them. There was a moment of confusion as they were overrun, White Buffalo remaining calm and luminous, Stone Hawk very nervous and unsure, and Fighting Calf completely terrified.

The youngest Shantee brave only motioned towards his hatchet when the first of four arrows tore into his body. A thickly muscled brave who had a mostly shaved head with one row of black hair down the center rode up to Fighting Calf as he writhed in pain. He raised his hatchet into the air and unleashed a terrible death blow into the side of the young brave's head, knocking him from his pony. He was dead before he hit the ground.

White Buffalo watched the spirit of his young friend dancing over his fallen body for a split second, then the spirit flew off into the clouds. He was not sad, knowing that Fighting Calf felt only a moment of pain. He had died the death of a warrior, and there was honor in that. Now he danced with his ancestors, and White Buffalo understood this. But Stone Hawk's face hardened and he growled, and even though he offered no physical resistance, a Mocktaw brave rode up to him and chopped deeply into his arm, knocking him off his pony.

So much of Stone Hawk's being had grown as he had learned to incorporate the Teachings into his life, but the terrible sight of his friend's body was more than he could bear. His old instincts had kicked in, and he wanted to kill them all. As he laid dazed on the ground, reeling from the intense pain, he came back to the thought, "Surrender and detach, all is on schedule."

Despite all that had happened in the last ten seconds around him, White Buffalo had not moved. He was still sitting on his pony, smiling, with his arms held out, palms facing the sky.

"Look at this stupid fool!" cried one brave to the man who had killed Fighting Calf. White Buffalo recognized this man as the leader, and he could understand their language though it was a strange dialect, much harsher sounding than the way his people spoke.

"We come in peace, with a message for your chief," said the Shantee medicine man.

"Did I ask you anything, fool?", came the reply from the leader. "You shut up, and you may live for a little while longer."

White Buffalo nodded silently. He looked at Stone Hawk who was bravely enduring his pain, and the wounded man closed his eyes. He heard White Buffalo in his mind say over and over, "do not fear, do not fear, do not fear." Two Mocktaw braves jumped off their ponies with the intent of killing Stone Hawk. White Buffalo closed his eyes and sent an intense telepathic message into the brain of the leader.

The leader shouted, "Do not kill him. Throw him on his pony, and kill him only if he gives us trouble!" The man then tilted his head oddly, as if he was surprised at his own words.

The two braves roughly threw the wounded Shantee upon his horse, and the whole group rode off into the direction of the Mocktaw village. White Buffalo prayed as they rode through the rain, silently reviewing the Teachings in his mind. He also focused on sending healing vibrations to Stone Hawk, who was riding slumped over on the pony's neck. He was holding his wounded arm with his other hand, trying to stop the bleeding, but it was a severe gash, and without attention, he would soon bleed to death.

They were approaching the side of a mountain and White Buffalo's attention was drawn upward. The sun had momentarily peeked out through the thick gray clouds, and its brilliance flashed on a pure white object at the mountain top. The Shantee medicine man realized that it was a person with white hair, and he tuned into the energy of this person. She was sitting facing away from them, but instantly turned and waved. Simultaneously, he heard the words, "Welcome and listen closely."

White Buffalo nodded once, and looked away from her, so that his connection to her would go unnoticed by his captors. He sent a telepathic response to verify what was happening. "Dear sister, is it you that I am hearing?", he sent the thought off on an imagined light ray.

A reply formed in his mind. "Yes, my brother, it is me. In a few moments you will be around the bend, so here is what you need to know. Crazy Eyes is smart and evil, but his thoughts can be read. Let me teach you how to tune into his thoughts or else your peace mission will fail."

"Around the bend, you will see an old huge rotting oak tree which stands at the edge of the forest near our village. This tree vibrates with the same energy patterns that the old wizard does. This tree became so large and strong that it began to obliterate all sunlight near it. The other, smaller trees, were in its shadow, and without light, they died. As this oak tree kept growing larger, thicker branches, more and more of the other trees and plants around it died. This tree soon became obsessed with its own power, and it relished its own ability to dominate the other growth in the forest. But the earth spirits felt its negative vibrations and they sent the rains which began to rot away the enormous tree's root base. Soon, its foundation was rotted, and last year a huge wind came and blew it over."

"It is only half alive now, and soon it will be no more than a memory. Crazy Eyes played in this tree as a boy. He had the seeds of dominance even then, but observing this tree and its own control over the forest, he mimicked it as the pattern for his own life. They still vibrate at the same frequency. Tune in to the tree, and you will be able to see what Crazy Eyes' real intentions are. I am Silver Fox, and I am with you. Go in peace."

This whole dialogue was revealed and retained in seconds through telepathy, and a moment later, White Buffalo spotted the huge fallen tree. It was enormous, and he tried to imagine how magnificent it must have been as it towered over this place for hundreds of years. As it fell, it had left a huge crater where the dirt had been. White Buffalo closed his eyes, and lowered the vibratory pattern of his mind and thoughts while projecting the idea "Great Oak, can you hear me?" He eventually heard a very deep voice speaking as if in slow motion.

"I was once the strongest, and now look at me. I'm almost dead, and for what?" complained the tree.

White Buffalo projected a thought back. "Great Oak brother, you are still great, but you did not know and honor the law. I bring these Teachings to the Mocktaws, and the Teaching that applies is 'Be someone who positively influences all life forms.' You killed others, broke the law, and now in your death, you will positively influence all life."

"How can I do that?" asked the tree.

"Millions of insects, many animals and countless

mosses and fungi will make you their home for the next thousand moons. You are not truly made up of wood and leaves, you are pure energy. That energy can never die, so there is nothing to fear. Know that you are loved, and goodbye for now," said the man. "Goodbye, and thank you," said the tree.

Many people were beginning to gather around them and White Buffalo knew they were close to the village. The people's faces were gaunt and their eyes betrayed a sadness. The children looked worn and thin, with ribs showing, but their smiles were still warmly innocent.

The war party rode into a village of hundreds and hundreds of tepees, and on down through what appeared to be the main route to the largest, most colorfully decorated tepee.

The leader of the war party dismounted and roughly pulled both Shantee men off their ponies. He had them stand outside the tepee as he entered for a moment, then he reappeared and pushed them through the entrance. There were eight men of differing ages sitting in a circle with a smoldering fire in the center. The leader of the war party took the vacant spot next to a man wearing one sparse-haired eagle feather. This man was obese, a quality that made him stand out because almost everyone else was very thin and lean. His complexion was pock-marked and wrinkled and one eye drifted off as he turned to behold the strangers. This was Crazy Eyes.

White Buffalo sensed that this was a man who could mercilessly kill, and the Shantee waited to be spoken to before he spoke. "What is your business in my country?" the old chief asked in a disinterested voice. As he said this, he waved his hand as if he really didn't care, but White Buffalo knew better.

"Chief Crazy Eyes, thank you for seeing us. I have been sent by my chief, Wolf with a Heart, who invites you to the harvest festival two moons from now." As he said this, the Shantee medicine man held the vision of the rotting old oak tree in his mind's eye. His vibrational thinking then adjusted and he instantly heard the old man's thoughts. "Who will attend and where is this festival to take place?" asked Crazy Eyes.

"All the leaders and chiefs from the other four nations will be present, and it will be held in the land of the Shantee, my home country." As he said this, White Buffalo heard the chief's thoughts say, "They want to lure me and my leaders away from our homes, kill us, and take over our country." White Buffalo quickly added, "We have gifts for you, may I get them?"

The chief's negative thoughts stopped for a moment and he said, "Gifts ...?" "They are in a bag on the side of my pony," said White Buffalo. Crazy Eyes merely gestured, and a grim-faced attendant sprang to his feet, fetched the bag, and returned with it. Stone Hawk was pale and sweating and needed attention immediately. White Buffalo was concerned for his friend, but knew the next few moments with the old wizard were critical.

The Shantee pulled out a generous piece of dried buffalo meat and a buffalo bladder filled with a milk and honey mixture. He heard the old man's thoughts say, "They're poisoned, he is an assassin!" So White Buffalo said, "I brought enough for you and I to eat together. May I serve you?"

This threw the old man off balance, for he reasoned that the food couldn't be poisoned if they were to share it. White Buffalo knelt down next to the chief, and tearing the meat in half, gave the bigger piece to Crazy Eyes. Without hesitation, the Shantee then began eating, and after a few bites, he noticed mouths watering and stomachs growling and passed the piece to the others until it was gone. The chief began eating heartily and the Shantee thought things were going well until he heard the thought, "I'll just kill them after I eat their food," emanate from the old man. At once, White Buffalo intuitively knew that the Mocktaw nation would not be able to grow with this man as their chief.

White Buffalo held the stones out to Crazy Eyes and said, "This is another gift from my chief to you. These stones represent more wealth to our people than any other object, even food." The old man looked at them and thought, "They're worthless junk, he must think I'm a fool." White Buffalo continued by saying, "I know as a chief and a medicine man that you know the hidden power of these stones, but I will reveal their exact nature for the others here who may not know."

The chief nodded with approval as this stranger acknowledged his wisdom. In truth, he had no idea what these stones with the strange markings were. The other Mocktaws present leaned closer to examine them, as they found themselves strangely comfortable with this man who had fed them. They were impressed with the way the stranger was gracefully handling their leader despite the shabby reception the Mocktaws had given them.

White Buffalo turned to address Crazy Eyes. "I

was mortally wounded in an accident, and as I lay near death, I had an intense vision. I was with our ancestors, all our ancestors, and they told me that my job on earth was to unite the five nations. They said I would need new laws to bring this to reality, and these laws would be called the Teachings for a New World. Each of these stones represents a different Teaching. Here, let me demonstrate how powerful they are."

He selected the yellow stone which had a sun on it. He took off his medicine bag which had the last remnants of the healing flower he had been given in the spirit world. He put the stone in the bag and said sacred words over it, then went over to Stone Hawk who was about to pass out from pain and blood loss. Despite this, he had never complained or made one sound since being struck. White Buffalo took the stone and ran it the length of the wound several times, and the wound began to sizzle and started to heal before their eyes. He tore a piece of material off his shirt and made a makeshift bandage by tying it around Stone Hawk's arm, then gently laid him down on nearby buffalo skins.

He had accomplished two things -- one, he helped Stone Hawk's immediate need; and two, he had impressed the power of the Teachings upon these men. But he had underestimated the need to be in control that fueled Crazy Eyes' inconsistent behavior. When White Buffalo returned to reading the old wizard's thoughts, they were not good. The old man had been upstaged, and he had a fragile psyche, which was quick to anger. He was about to explode when White Buffalo quickly said, "In my vision, there were many good Mocktaw spirits who encouraged me to seek you out to heal the old wound between our people. They told me to use the stones to heal the ancient wound between us in the same way that the stone healed my friend's arm."

Something then happened that could only be divine order. With the exception of Crazy Eyes, all the other Mocktaws present gathered around White Buffalo. The Shantee medicine man must have been so convincing and emitted such a positive vibration, that those love-starved people couldn't help themselves. They sensed the genuine desire this stranger had to right the ancient wrongs and they unknowingly gave him more attention than their chief. Crazy Eyes exploded in anger.

"These two are assassins! They come with their lies to trick me and my council of elders to leave our people in their time of need! They plan on fattening us up in their country and then they will kill us. This one has tricked the thunder beings to curse us with rain every day, and in the same way he has put a spell on you fools. Look at you! You're ready to do whatever he says. He comes in here with a magic trick and some rocks. Well, I don't believe it. His tribe and the other three have always hated us because we are strong. They pretend to be peaceful and wise, well, I can tell you they weren't very peaceful the day they drove an arrow into your father's head!"

The old wizard pointed to the leader of the war party who had killed Fighting Calf. The brave came back to his anger which was his old familiar way, and jumped to his feet, pulling out his tomahawk. "I have made my decision. If you are truly the chosen one, you will no doubt pass the test. If you falter, I will kill your friend slowly in front of you. Your fate will not be so simple. Prepare the fire pit!" said the old man angrily.

The other braves were confused as their allegiance was in doubt, but the killer of Fighting Calf pulled Stone Hawk to his feet, and shoved him and White Buffalo out of the tepee. He bound their hands tightly with leather cord and tied them to a stake. There was much shouting and many squaws came running to begin building a blazing fire in a long rectangular dugout with rocks at the bottom. "It looks like it ends here, my brother," said Stone Hawk.

"Surrender and Detach, for all is on schedule" came the reply from White Buffalo. "All truly is on schedule, my friend. Do not fear, we will succeed! Now, they must not see us talking, go inward, do your sacred sitting to connect with the mind of Great Spirit. All is perfection. I give you my word." Stone Hawk thanked his ancestors for giving him a mentor and friend like White Buffalo.

8
CHILDREN OF THE SUN

The fire burned deep into the night and the two Shantees could see the red hot rocks at the bottom of the pit. All concept of time was suspended, for during sacred sitting, time truly ceases to exist. The next thing they knew, Stone Hawk was positioned at one end of the fire pit, and his friend was positioned at the other end. The pit was very long, enough to hold thirty-five to forty tepees end to end. On each side of Stone Hawk was a wild-eyed Mocktaw brave, while White Buffalo stood alone at the opposite end. The Shantee medicine man looked across the pit and could see the shimmering image of his friend and he smiled.

The whole village surrounded this scene and the elders and Crazy Eyes were seated half-way down the fire pit. "This man says he is here to unite the five nations, but he lies. He is here to kill me and the council and to conquer you. He has claimed to be chosen by our ancestors. If this is true, he will walk the coals unharmed. If he does not, we will cut his friend's head off and feed him to the dogs!" said the chief.

"My cousins! Your ancestors asked me to give you this message." White Buffalo spoke, looking around with his arms held out to his sides. "Our fathers gave me Teachings by which you will be happy, have full bellies, live to become gray hairs and hold your grandchildren. LISTEN TO ME AND THINK! I bring peace and love, I am not your enemy. Fear is the enemy, love is the cure." He put his hands together in reverence, saw his father smiling down from the cloud filled black sky. A glow surrounded him as he stepped down into the pit. In his mind, he was stepping into a cool stream and he visualized the water and the slippery rocks. He kept walking and the people began talking. "Is this a holy man?" they asked. They had seen members of their own clan who broke the chief's inconsistent laws walk the pit, and each time the person wound up charred beyond recognition. As he was halfway down the pit directly in front of Crazy Eyes, the old wizard threw some yellow powder in front of White Buffalo. It flashed and puffed foul smelling smoke, momentarily breaking his concentration. He felt searing heat, but instantly repeated "Fear is the enemy, Love is the cure," and his mother's face appeared smiling, and he continued to walk.

He was nearing the end of the pit when a young brave seeking to get in good standing with Crazy Eyes took a long tree limb and crashed it down on White Buffalo's head.   He stopped, bowed slightly from the blow, and continued. He looked up to see Stone Hawk only a few feet away and stepped up out of the pit.   He had a few blisters from the momentary lapse created by the wizard's trickery, but he was virtually unscathed.

The people began cheering! Crazy Eyes sensed a shift in power and he stormed off into the night. The braves who had flanked Stone Hawk at his end of the pit took the two Shantees away, but this time they were not roughed up and shoved.   They were treated with respect, and were brought to a small tepee at the edge of the village nearest the woods. They entered to find an old woman sitting with a beautiful young lady. They looked to be sacred sitting, and the girl said, "My mother welcomes you, please sit."   The old woman opened her eyes and smiled. She began a series of odd gestures to her daughter, who kept nodding and then the girl turned to the Shantees to relay the message.

"My mother's name is Silver Fox. She says that you are the wind that has come to blow over the rotten oak tree named Crazy Eyes. The people of the village are beginning to shift to your side, and you are in grave danger because of this.   The council of elders are split on what to do, and Crazy Eyes still controls the strongest braves led by Mountain Lion, who killed your friend.   My mother has asked me to have you explain these Teachings and how you used them today."

White Buffalo said, "The first Teaching from the North is to know the difference between right and wrong. Your people are suffering, and that is wrong. You and I are to put an end to that suffering, which is right. No matter who is creating that suffering, it is wrong, and if they are ending suffering, it is right."

"The second Teaching from the South says fear is the enemy, love is the cure. Fear is darkness and love is the light; the light shines and all things are then seen clearly. This is the principle that must first be learned by all people. The light is always shining, but sometimes obstructions come between us and the sun, which creates shadow or darkness. Sun is Great Spirit. Shadow is only an illusion, but the sun warms us, grows our crops, dries our meat. The only enemy is the shadow, the fear. Love cures every wound."

"The third Teaching from the East is to do what has to be done when it has to be done. As the war party overran us, I felt Fighting Calf's terror, and could sense he would go for his weapon. I knew he was about to die. I had to hold the sacred seat knowing it was imperative that I remain luminous and still. It was difficult to do so while my dear friend was cut to pieces, but I did what had to be done immediately because it was for the highest good. Had I not, we would all be vulture food in the desert right now and our mission could never be completed."

"Teaching Four from the West is ..." The old woman held up her hand and White Buffalo stopped. Silver Fox began communicating to her daughter who relayed this message. "My mother knows the fourth Teaching concerns respecting all life, and she will help you tomorrow through the execution of this principle." Silver Fox motioned White Buffalo to continue and he did.

The fifth Teaching is that life works to the extent you keep your word. After our failed meeting with Crazy Eyes today, we were tied to a stake. I was feeling shaky, so I gave my word to Stone Hawk that all was going according to plan. I always keep my word, and in this way I convinced my thoughts to follow my words. The truth sets up a vibration of clarity that is imperative to any successful endeavor. I see through the lies of people quite easily because I have become established in the truth."

He continued on, "The sixth Teaching from the Down direction is that to believe is great, but to know makes it so. This teaching saved me in the fire pit. My love was carrying me until Crazy Eyes threw the powder, which broke my concentration. I instantly had a choice to make. I chose to KNOW that the heat and fire were the illusion, that my knowingness was the only reality. Through practice, this discipline has given me the ability to give myself a command, and to follow it."

Each time White Buffalo explained a Teaching, he placed the stone that symbolized that Teaching into the hands of Silver Fox. As he gave her each stone, she would hold it to her face, rubbing it on her cheek, or cradle it lovingly in her hands. This made White Buffalo smile. He did not expect to meet one so evolved in the Mocktaw race. He was almost embarrassed that he had thought in this limited way.

"The last Teaching is the seventh, from the Center direction. It says to surrender and detach for all is on schedule. This concept teaches us to act, without attachment to the fruit of our actions. It teaches us to know that Great Spirit is always present, orchestrating every move in the dance. Knowing this, brings us to a place of peace and trust. By your vibration, you know this place well. Am I right, Silver Fox?" She smiled and nodded.

The conversation continued in this enlightened fashion for a time, then the braves poked their heads in the tepee, and motioned to the Shantees that it was time to go. The wise ones exchanged hugs and thanks, and the braves took them back to the stake and loosely tied them to it. The Mocktaws did so apologetically, and bowed to them as they left, saying "Goodnight cousins."

They were awakened by the sounds of shouting and drumming. Unfamiliar braves tore them off the stake, treating them rougher than any had before. They were poked and pushed by spears all the way through the village, and they came to a large clearing where the whole village had once again assembled. There was a headless body tied to a stake, with its severed head, hands and feet laying near it. White Buffalo recognized the face, which blankly stared to nowhere, as one of the braves who brought them to Silver Fox's tepee. The second brave was standing in front of Crazy Eyes, who looked angry and weary. The council of elders surrounded him, but certain members were noticeably absent.

Crazy Eyes spoke. "You have proved that your allegiance lies with the treacherous strangers. So be it. I want them to see what happens to those who choose to betray me." He clapped his hands twice, and forty braves formed two lines with twenty men in each line. The brave accused of treason screamed and ran between them. They quickly pulled out tomahawks and spears and began striking him. Blow by terrible blow rained down upon him until he fell to the ground, mortally wounded. The tormentors then surrounded him and quickly ended his life.

Some villagers began crying, others howled or groaned in anguish, and the crowd became restless. They had seen enough butchery to last a lifetime. The fat old tyrant motioned for White Buffalo to come forward. The gauntlet reassembled on command. He smiled and said, "It's your turn," in a sing-song voice.

White Buffalo took his place at the mouth of the gauntlet, when an unearthly howl came from the edge of the woods. The whole tribe turned their faces at exactly the same time to see an old white haired woman running very fast directly towards the opposite end of the gauntlet. White Buffalo saw that it was Silver Fox and he screamed "No, save yourself my friend!" She ran like the wind and as she was almost to the killers, they raised their weapons in anticipation of the kill. She let out a second unearthly howl and from out of nowhere, hundreds of wolves raced towards the braves in the lines, two sometimes three wolves savagely ripping each man to pieces. It was an awful sight to behold. The villagers were screaming and running in any direction that took them far away from the slaughter. The wolves knew who to attack by the frequency of vibration that a killer possesses. They had been taught to only destroy the killers, and that is what they did. The huge leader of the pack, Blackie, ran right up to Crazy Eyes and tore him to pieces in a frightful instant. With amazing speed and force, the killers were vanquished and Silver Fox cried a different guttural scream and the wolves became passive, their ears went back, and they sat back on their haunches. Blackie quickly ran to Silver Fox's side and sat down as she began fondly stroking his head while he licked her hand.

* * *

The bodies of the dead were burned at a mass funeral pyre. The Mocktaw people restructured the council of elders, who unanimously decided to make Silver Fox their leader. Stone Hawk and several Mocktaw braves brought the message of what had transpired back to the Shantees. They also told Wolf with a Heart that Silver Fox had asked White Buffalo to stay and hold daily learning circles to most effectively impart the Teachings to the Mocktaw people.

Wolf with a Heart had Stone Hawk bring back four wagons that contained food. The Mocktaw people were slowly but surely learning to incorporate the lessons in their day to day life. They were shocked, but grateful for the gifts of food and knowledge gladly given by the Shantee people.

The more the people lived the Teachings, the milder the weather became, and the sun began to shine almost every day. It was too late in the growing season to re-plant, and that was a major concern for it would be impossible to survive an entire winter with no food. Silver Fox and White Buffalo reminded the Mocktaws to apply Teaching Seven, to surrender and detach for all is truly on schedule. Most of the villagers did not believe or understand this, but their faith in their leaders was so strong, they just trusted.

Silver Fox's daughter, Words of the Fox, found herself spending countless hours with White Buffalo as she translated her mother's words. A wonderful romance began blossoming between them that was a joy for all to see. He knew much about teaching love, but she taught him about romantic love. These two young people had previously been so immersed in their missions, that they had never experienced the joy of sharing life with a lover. Now they were together, and they fit like soul mates.

White Buffalo found himself in an unfamiliar role, that of the student. He was not uncomfortable in this role, only awkward and unsure of himself, more like a little child first learning to walk. They were the kind of couple that made people feel a glow just by being in their presence.

White Buffalo stayed with the Mocktaws until it was time for the harvest festival. He and Words of the Fox, Silver Fox and the entire Mocktaw council made the journey to the Shantee country to attend. Fifteen or twenty children and adults who had taken to the Teachings like second nature also were asked to go. When the entourage was greeted like long lost friends, they were bursting with joy.

Wolf with a Heart himself rode out to meet them and lead them into the village. The moment they arrived, the whole village broke into song. Smiles were everywhere and also many tears. The other three visiting nations were already in attendance, and now the circle was complete.

It was a sight to make hairs stand on end and even the most powerful people felt honored to be present. Wolf with a Heart had organized the evening's festivities and after all had rested, a huge fire was built in the clearing next to the village. The Savitris, Weekamocks, and the Matabas also brought forty or fifty representatives and their councils. All the chiefs got together in the early evening for "Sacred Sitting" and to smoke.

Wolf with a Heart stood and said, "Welcome, my brothers and sisters and thank you for coming. Our ancestors are smiling and dancing, for we have made their dreams come true. Our cousins, the Mocktaws, have suffered greatly, but their rightful leader is in place and here today. After conferring with the other chiefs, we all agree that the food that has been stockpiled will be taken back to the Mocktaws so they can survive the winter." The Shantee chief turned to face Silver Fox and bowed deeply to honor her. Tears formed in her eyes and she smiled broadly. She could not talk, but she could sing, and as she began singing, they all joined in. They sat in silence for a long while, and then Silver Fox, with her eyes closed, began making odd gestures to her daughter. Wolf with a Heart asked Words of the Fox to translate her mother's gestures. She said that she understood the message, but it was not coming from Silver Fox. They all looked at Silver Fox, who was deep in trance, as if her body was with them, but her spirit was somewhere else. The hand gestures continued and her daughter translated.

"I am the mother of you all, and you have done well. I am Chantisita, the mother of the People and you are my children who make me more than proud. Tonight in heaven, we are having a festival, too. All those who could not attend on earth, are dancing with joy in heaven right now. All the old wounds are healed, and ancient enemies now call each other brother. There are many cycles to life, my children, and we must never forget the Teachings. They must be faithfully and accurately passed down to your children, who must also learn the importance of teaching their children so we do not grow fat and lazy again. Look towards the morning sky."

The whole group got up and looked eastward. "You will see a star moving slowly and brightly." Their eyes began scanning the heavens. "There it is!" said White Buffalo, who pointed excitedly. Words of the Fox continued her translation. "The uniting of the Five Nations has torn a hole in the dense aura of fear that formerly surrounded this world, and this star represents something very meaningful. Your brothers and sisters on the other side of the world are suffering, and tonight their savior is born. This child is born on the other side of the world to bring the Teachings for a New World to that area of the planet. This would not have happened so soon without you, because your actions and your love built the bridge that connected heaven and earth. I tell you this because you are only learning that your love affects every soul positively, just as your fear affects them negatively. All souls are invisibly connected to each other, which is what we call Great Spirit. Great Spirit is the merger point of all our souls! This energy exists within us, and without us. When many come together under the pretense of love, as you in the five nations have done tonight, this white light energy is magnified more than you could ever know. The power of what you have done and are doing is being felt and appreciated in a multitude of realms and worlds throughout the universe. Never forget how proud of you we are, for you have accomplished something that reaches deeply into the hearts of others. On their present course, your brothers and sisters on the other side of the world will need almost twenty-five thousand moons to accomplish what you have done in the last five generations. We tell you this only for you to acknowledge yourselves for your greatness, and continue to do more of the same.

There is no higher gift than to bring love, light, and laughter into the life of another and that is truly what you have magnificently done. Never stop learning and teaching, for if you do, we are destined to repeat this cycle of darkness. You are pure energy; you can never die! Take this thought and may it bring you solace. You came into your current life to earn the right to merge, as one, into the limitless body of Great Spirit. In doing so, you have made the lives of all souls more meaningful. At every moment in life we have a choice. Forget none of it, forgive all of it, choose wisely, and most importantly - love yourself and each other always."

PART TWO

The Teachings in

the New World

9

AN ACCIDENT WAITING TO HAPPEN

It was the sound of his own screaming that woke him up. Wilson Raintree sat up out of bed holding his face in his hands. His body was soaked with perspiration, his legs tangled in a sheet, and his head was pounding.

He looked past the half empty tequila bottle to the clock on the dresser. He caught a glimpse of himself in the mirror, and shook his head at the sight. His once handsome face was swollen and there were deep bags under his eyes. The three-day growth of stubble on his face made him look unrecognizable, even to himself.

It can't be eleven-thirty already, he thought. He dropped down on the bed, depression swelling inside of him at the thought of facing another day on this case. Resigning to the hopelessness of the moment, he decided to go back to sleep.

He awoke to the phone ringing, and growled a deep, gravelly, "Hello."

"Billy?   Are you still in bed?" Jenny asked incredulously.

"Naw, Jen, I'm just feeling a little sick today so I decided to take the day off."

"Well, that's funny, cause I just called the office and Marge said they had no idea where you were and hadn't heard from you yet today. Are you drinking again, Billy?", concern edged with suspicion in her voice.

"No, Jenny - NO!", he yelled, sitting up on the edge of his bed, putting his feet on the floor. "I don't need this from you today, Jen. I really don't. Here I am sick and you accuse me of that! Let's not have this conversation, OK?" He realized he was yelling, and he softened his voice and spoke. "I need you babe, when are you coming home?"

There was silence on the other end of the phone. "Billy ..." Jen was speaking firmly and quietly. "We've been all through this. You know I'm not coming home. We've tried this so many times, and we both agreed that my moving out is for our mutual good. Please don't open up this conversation again. It's been six weeks, Billy, and I've got to tell you that I've never been clearer in my life. I've never felt more on my mission and filled with purpose than right now. So please don't start that same old conversation that tears us both apart, please." she asked with true sincerity.

Billy felt tears coming but he pushed them back.

"You're right, Jen, I'm sorry," he said with genuine remorse. "It's just that this case is going down the drain and the people on the reservation have put all their faith in me, and I'm terrified at the thought of letting them down. I'm the big lawyer for the people who was going to beat the government and win one for the good guys. Instead, I lost you and I'm losing the case ...", his voice trailed off.

Jenny Raintree felt like running to his side and soothing away his troubles as she had done many times before. But then she steeled herself by remembering that this was exactly where they had always gotten stuck in their relationship. If they could evolve beyond the point where Billy would intentionally sabotage himself, compelling her to act as his savior, they could salvage their marriage. But they were still in the midst of this difficult dance, and she felt a sort of guilt at not being there for him.

"It's not about losing me, Billy. It's about finding yourself." Jen said tenderly.

"How is it that you always say the perfect thing?", he asked in tired wonderment.

Not answering his question, she said, "Billy, I need to come over to get a few of my things. Is now a good time? If not, I can come later."

"Give me a half-hour, Jen, OK?" They agreed and hung up.

Feeling hung over, he dragged himself out of bed and into the shower. As the cool water ran over his body, his mind drifted back to why he woke up screaming. What was that dream that had scared him so much? The more he tried to recall the source of his fear, the further away the recollection went from his conscious mind.

He let it go, and thought about the legal case --
representing his people against a government with a long-
standing history of Native American abuse. He was hired
by the elders of the Rosebud reservation in South Dakota,
who had begun building a gambling casino on prime Native
American land where the Missouri River and the White
River meet. Casinos had begun sprouting up all over the
country when Native American lawyers had found a
loophole in government policies regarding the Indians. The
loophole stated that the United States gambling and tax laws
were exempt on the reservations. The casinos provided
hundreds of jobs for the people, and solved the serious fiscal
problems that most reservations had always experienced.

The casino and roads had already been constructed
with a restaurant, hotel, and accompanying parking lots
soon to be finished, when federal agents appeared with a
previously undiscovered land map claiming that the casino
and half the hotel had been built on U.S. soil. If this were
true, the tribe and the Native American employees would be
subject to taxation, and instead of hiring only Native
Americans, a certain amount of jobs would have to be filled
by people of other ethnic backgrounds because of
Affirmative Action.

Billy allowed himself to be consumed in the
discovery process of the case, and it was then that he and
Jenny had hit the wall in their marriage. They began to see
how different they were when he was away for long periods
of time researching which treaties and land maps were valid.

He was the son of full-blooded Lakota Sioux parents,
and she was the daughter of a white man who had fallen in

love and married a Lakota Sioux woman. Though a full-blooded Sioux, he grew up interested in sports, big-business and politics, leaving the reservation for college on a football scholarship, and then on to law school. Because he loved competition, acquisition, and material things, a career as a legal eagle fueled those fires within him.

Jenny grew up as her mother's daughter, deeply tied to the traditions and history of the Lakotas, and well aware of the difficulties of reservation life. They met in college, and almost immediately fell in love. After Billy passed the South Dakota bar exam, they were married.

She was an artist and musician, interested in enhancing the lives of all people by preserving the beauty of the ways and teachings of her people.

He was an opportunist and a pragmatic person, inspired by big money cases and front page headlines. They were a great team together because love transcended their differences and each became a more well-balanced person through the influence of the other. He taught her discipline, organization, and business principles. She taught him about meditation and appreciation of music and nature.

For the first five years of their marriage, they prospered and built their own home in Pierre, the state capital. She had worked on the reservation selling her pottery and drawings, and played her flute in a band at night. It was a Native American band called 'Red Road', and at first they had few gigs, but through persistence, they eventually developed a large following, playing several good paying engagements every week.

As her success grew, Billy began drinking and losing high-profile cases. If she was playing in a bar, he would come in and play the jealous husband, over drinking and being loud. The downward cycle of his career was in full bloom when her father, who was a land developer, brought Billy in for seemingly simple legal counsel regarding the contracts to begin building the casino. Billy was grateful and had cleaned up his act, doing a competent job despite unchallenging circumstances, when the federal agents threw them a curve with their claim of a land dispute. He was retained to resolve what at first appeared to be an open and shut case, but in the process, he and Jenny began having problems.

They decided on a temporary separation. The following week, he lost the first court battle in a pre-trial hearing when he tried to have the federal map thrown out as evidence on the grounds that it was invalid. He had lost so few times early in his career, and now he mused at how accustomed he had become to losing.

He turned off the shower, dried himself, and began to lather his face to shave. Just then he had a vision of the dream from the night before. He was walking through vaguely familiar woods, when he heard a crash and turned to see a huge white buffalo charging right at him. He ran but the white buffalo was gaining on him. At the moment he was about to be run over, he woke up. It was so realistic, thinking about it now made him sweat.

Suddenly, his thoughts were interrupted by the doorbell, and his heart began beating for he knew it was Jenny.

He yelled, "Just a minute, Jen!" He didn't want her to see him so disheveled, so he buttoned up a shirt, put on underwear, and had one leg in his pants, hopping on one foot to answer the door. He quickly thrust the bare leg into the other leg of his pants when he stumbled and crashed head first into the door.

He got up dazed, feeling stupid and dizzy, and trying to compose himself, opened the door with as debonair a hello as he could muster. Jenny looked at him and laughed. "What in God's name happened to you?"

Billy had his shirt buttoned in the wrong holes, there was shaving cream beneath one ear , and he had blood dripping down his chin from a shaving cut. His hair was slicked back like a gangster, he was sweating bullets on his forehead, on which there was a rapidly growing bump from smacking into the door. She put her hand to her mouth to try to stop giggling, but couldn't.

"My God, she's beautiful, and I look like a bum," he thought to himself. She looked around and stopped herself from making a derisive comment about his housekeeping. "I know the place looks rough, honey, I'm sorry." She stood there, looking around, and the awkwardness of the moment just hung in the air. "Would you like some coffee?", he asked breaking the silence.

"Decaf tea would be nice if you have it."

"There may be some left over from when you were here. I'm not sure," he said, fumbling through the cupboards for it.

"I think I know where some is. May I look?" He shrugged his shoulders, nodding yes, but feeling lost in his own house. She quickly found the tea and began preparing it. As they were drinking the tea, they talked about the case. "I'm sorry to hear you lost the pre-trial hearing."

"That's OK. Thanks for the sympathy. Judge Austin

heard the motion, and denied it. I don't blame him, I didn't have enough evidence to warrant him dismissing the federal map as invalid."

"How did this mess happen, Billy?"

"Do you have time to hear the story?" She nodded yes as she sipped her tea.

"The elders elected Joe Black Eagle to head the casino construction committee, and your father and he began accepting contract bids for the work. That's when the Committee brought me in to make sure all the bids, land searches, and appropriate documents conformed to state and federal law.

"Joe Black Eagle and I had the county surveyor go over the maps to be certain of where our land began and ended, then we staked it off in the spring of last year. We went by the state map, which the surveyor told us was a duplicate of the federal map. We chose Black Elk Point as the sight for the project, because it protrudes into a big beautiful bend in the Missouri River, offering a fabulous view of the river in both directions, as well as the beginning of the Black Hills.

"The county surveyor staked it off, the state land assay office approved our blueprint, and we broke ground in May. We finished the casino in late August and were half-way done with the hotel and restaurant when an agent from Washington came up to Joe with a stop work order. They produced a version of the original map of the 1887 treaty that granted this land to the Lakotas. It showed that what is now Black Elk Point was under water back then. The building of the Oahe Dam up river in 1947 lowered the river level twenty-five feet, creating what is now a part of Black Elk Point.

"The high water mark on the Missouri river is federal property, and since the water used to be up that high, where the hotel and restaurant now sit is supposedly federal land. The lead officer for the Bureau of Land Management is a man named Mason Williams. He's very hard-nosed, and not only applied for a motion to make us disassemble our buildings and move them, but has asked Judge Austin to levy a stiff fine on the Committee for disturbing federal wetlands."

"I thought all land to the North and East of the river belongs to us."

"That is true, but the loophole according to Williams and his lawyers is the high water mark claim. It's a gray area in the treaty, with no precedent on the books. My concern is not knowing what kind of pressure is being put on the judge to decide this case expeditiously."

"The government can't possibly want more bad press concerning Indian Affairs, could they?"

"No, but a five hundred thousand dollar fine would be a nice source of revenue for the feds. That kind of fine would surely cripple this project, which we do not need. I don't need it, and I don't know if I can handle it," said Billy in a depressed tone.

"Of course you can handle it. You were chosen, therefore, you must be the right person. Don't you see, Billy?" she said with childlike enthusiasm. "Wakan-Tanka never gives us more than we can handle, this I know."

"Yeah, right, Jen. I hate it when you give me that New Age mumbo-jumbo."

"New Age? When you stop feeling so sorry for yourself and get on with what you're here for, you'll see that the sacred tradition of our people is absolutely consistent with the teachings of Jesus Christ, Buddha, the Blessed Virgin, and every other saint and deity throughout time. Quit complaining about your problems, Billy. If you don't like it, create something better. This is why I had to leave! Neither one of us can evolve unless we move beyond the game where you crash and I put it all back together and make it better. If we stay there, we both miss the lesson. Well, I won't have any part of it," she said indignantly.

"Wait, Jen, I'm sorry ..."

"No! I suggest you go to Broken Rock Mountain and take some time to figure out what you're going to do, because I won't watch you destroy yourself any more. By the way, Billy. You're sweating out last night's booze. I can smell it. Don't stop drinking for me. I don't care if you drink. You're only lying to yourself. I'll get my things later. I gotta go." She got up and gracefully made a quick exit without even slamming the door.

Billy let out a scream and smashed the cups of tea off the table in complete frustration. He ran to the bedroom deciding that it was time to finish off the bottle of tequila. He went to the dresser drawer, pulled out the bottle, and, as he raised it to his lips, he happened to see himself in the mirror. He looked at this stranger with a liquor bottle staring out of the mirror and he was repulsed. He hurled the bottle at the mirror, and slumped down on the floor in total frustration.

His mind was reeling as he inventoried the major events of his life. His many early successes - football, college, winning Jen as his wife, his early legal career - it all came so easily. Then the last two years of hell - Jenny being out with the band, not there for him; losing his first huge case, followed by another, then another. Those losses had changed people's perception of him. The lost money made him change the way he looked at himself.

He observed that those two things were so important to him that without them, his life was worthless. He had put more importance on his image and his net worth, than he gave to his marriage and most importantly, to himself. He made a decision. He decided to not care what people thought of him. He decided to get help, but where could he go?

He held out his arms and asked out loud, "OK, God, where do I go?"

He sat there and no answer came. He decided to clean up the broken mirror and tea cups, and to open some windows to let fresh air blow through the house. He did so, and after cleaning up, he decided to call the office for his messages. A wind came in through the window and blew over a framed picture that Jenny had arranged on a table in the dining room.

He wondered how only one picture among ten or twelve could blow over, and he picked it up. It was Grandmother Kawaylu. Crazy old woman, he thought to himself, and then he stopped. That's what he always said about her, because she consulted the spirit world before acting. She was always burning something, or carrying a piece of dead animal in what she called a medicine bag around her neck. But the more he thought about it, she was there for him at every critical juncture in his life. He almost felt embarrassed that he hadn't made the time to visit her for more than a year, though she lived so close by. Now it was time. He thought to himself, "Should I call first? No, I'll just go there." He hopped in his car and drove until he found himself on the bumpy dirt road that led to his grandmother's house.

He knocked on his mother's mother's door, and waited. He knocked again and no one came. He went around to the back of the house which bordered the woods and he saw her sitting on a tree stump, saying some words. He approached very quietly, and got within twenty feet of her, and still she didn't turn around. She kept right on speaking her Lakota words, which he was now close enough to hear, but couldn't understand. He was saddened, for in days passed, she would have sensed his presence much sooner, but now she was old, and was no longer as perceptive as before.

"You still make more noise than a moose in the woods, Wilson," said Grandmother without turning around.

Most people called him Billy, but she had always called him Wilson, and he hoped she always would. "How long did you know I was standing here?"

"That's not important now, is it, Wilson? You have worked hard to live the life of a Washishu (white man) and shun the ways of the Lakota. How is it working for you?"

"That's not true Grandmother, I ... "

"Oh Wilson, don't lie me. I'm too old," she said impatiently. "I heard you drove Jenny off and that you're getting your butt kicked in court, right?"

He sat down in the grass at her feet and said, "Grandmother, don't swear like that. It doesn't sound good coming from you!"

"Wilson, I want you to listen. I'm leaving soon, this I know. You've been working in the negative, and until you bottom out, you won't turn the corner. Pain makes us turn the corner. It is Great Spirit's way of driving us to seek knowledge and wisdom. Have you had enough pain yet?" she asked with love.

"Yes, Grandmother."

"Good. What you must do is sit on your problems in nature. The vibration of nature will cleanse this limited city vibration from your energy field. This is where to start. Three days on Broken Rock Mountain. Go right now, Wilson."

"No, Grandmother. I can't. You don't understand, I have the case, my situation with Jenny, people are counting on me."

"Oh, then you haven't had enough pain yet. OK, do as you wish." She got up and began walking towards the house. He got up to follow her saying, "Wait, Grandmother."

"I have nothing more to say to you, boy. You visit me now because you're in trouble and you don't know where to turn. Because I love you, I give you answers, and you don't obey. You know what? You never did. Not as a child, not as a youth, not as a young man, and not now. You know what else, Wilson? I normally don't allow people with your vibration in my energy field, because they are an accident waiting to happen. Either do as I say, or take your accident elsewhere. I don't want it happening on my lawn." She slowly walked away and into the house.

He walked back to his car in a state of numbness,

and drove back home. He reflected on the day's events, and it had not been one of the better days in his life. He made some dinner, and sat in the darkness, just thinking.

He fell asleep in his living room chair and began dreaming. He was walking in the familiar woods again, the air was cool and fresh and all was peaceful. He heard a crashing sound and as he turned in the direction of the noise, he saw a huge white buffalo charging at him, and he began running. The animal was gaining on him as he recognized people in his life observing the chase as if on the sidelines of a football field. Couldn't they see he needed help? He saw his parents first and he reached out his hand for them to pull him to safety, but they just began laughing. He saw high school friends, people on his college football team, buddies from law school, all standing and laughing as he ran for his life from the white buffalo. The last two people he saw were Jenny and Grandmother Kawaylu. They wanted to help, but deep inside he got the feeling that they couldn't. He somehow knew that to help him meant compromising their life path. He'd had enough running. He stopped and turned to face the stampeding behemoth. Instead of trampling him, the animal nudged him up into the air with its nose, and he was now riding on its back at full speed.

He didn't know where he was, but he wasn't afraid until he saw the edge of a cliff get closer and closer. The white buffalo didn't slow down, but kept going faster and faster until it reached the edge of the precipice where the beast came to an instant stop. When the animal stopped completely, Billy's body was thrown over the edge and he felt himself falling down, down, down ...

He woke up screaming again, scared out of his mind. He didn't sleep the rest of the night, and waited until eight a.m. to call Jenny.

He told her of his meeting with Grandmother and how she had told him to go to Broken Rock Mountain just as Jenny had. He was packed and wanted to call her so she could get her things from the house before he left for three days. She said she would be over after she meditated, by about nine o'clock, and he resisted slightly. She said that she had to meditate and that if he needed to go, she would understand. He decided to wait for her, and they hung up.

The doorbell rang at five after nine, and when he opened the door, Jenny noticed a look of grim resolution on her husband's face.

"Are you OK, Billy?"

"I've been having recurring nightmares, and sleep is becoming a rare commodity these days."

"If you allow it, I may be able to give you some clarity about the meaning of the dream." He hesitated for a moment, then decided to go ahead and tell her, maybe she could help.

"First, I'm walking in a woods that feels very safe to me, when a white buffalo appears and begins chasing me as if to kill me. This happened a few separate nights, and each time it came closer to trampling me. Then last night, friends from various periods in my life appeared and were watching me being chased, and as I asked for their help, they only laughed, and turned away. The only ones who wanted to help were you and Grandmother, but I knew inside that helping me would be a backwards step in your own personal evolution, so you couldn't help either. I had enough, and stopped running. The white buffalo didn't kill me. Instead it threw me on its back and took me on a high speed ride, right up to the edge of a cliff. Then it stopped on a dime, and I went flying over the edge. I kept on falling, and I felt that if I hit bottom, I would really be dead. Then I woke up screaming, as I did the night before last." He became silent and looked down at his hands as he kept nervously rubbing them together. Jenny thoughtfully nodded for a minute.

"The safety of the woods represents your comfort zone, or your life as you've known it for the past thirty-five years. The white buffalo is a sacred symbol to our people of the beginning of a new way of life. These people who appeared, the ones who laughed at your needing their help, who were they?"

"First, my parents, then sports' friends, law school buddies and finally my current colleagues," he said. She swallowed hard and put her hand to her chin, as if wrestling with what to say. "I think the people who were laughing represent the cast of characters in your life who are unwilling and incapable of helping you or anyone. They are most likely embroiled in their own life soup of problems that has only one answer - to connect with spirit. All except your parents, Billy, and this is hard for me to say, but you need to hear it. You are their golden boy, they did everything for you, even to the exclusion of your brother's and sister's feelings. Though they treated you specially, you never thanked them. If you did, I never saw it, and I have to say that you broke their hearts," she said, looking him right in the eyes.

He avoided her gaze, knowing what she said was

true. He started to defend his actions to himself internally. His parents and he were in two different worlds - they sent smoke signals, he sent faxes. They traded ponies, he traded euro-bonds. His thoughts were interrupted by Jen.

"You'll have time to justify all of this to yourself later. Do you want me to stop now, or finish the dream interpretation?"

"Please continue, Jen," he weakly replied.

"Grandmother and I can't help because we love you too much to try to force you to be what you are not." she said. "Once you faced your fear, you found yourself carried by the white buffalo to the cliff and thrown off. It was the death of the false you, or your ego." She looked at him and his face showed confusion. "Here's the bottom line. You must move out of your comfort zone if you are to achieve happiness and purpose in this lifetime. Great Spirit, in the guise of a white buffalo, is prompting you to change your old circle of friends because they are just as confused as you, if not more so.

"Your parents, grandmother and myself represent an opportunity to evolve by healing old wounds. The white buffalo represents spirit as a vehicle to conquer your ego, because by doing so, you become Godlike. Does that make sense to you?" she asked.

"I never thought I'd be saying this, but it feels right inside though I really don't understand it."

"That's called sympathetic resonance. You raised your vibratory awareness to the wavelength at which I was communicating and the vibrations became one as your wavelength matched mine. This is an excellent beginning,

Billy." Her saying those words opened hope within him of a possible reunion between them.

"Would you like to join me in the woods, Jenny? ... We could have a really good time ..."

"Billy! You just backslided into your ego,. It's not about me joining you, it's about you becoming who you really are. I need to get a couple of boxes in the attic, then I have to go to band rehearsal." She got up and went upstairs, and soon returned with a couple of boxes of clothes and books which Billy helped her load into the car.

"One last thing, Billy. I suggest that you get together with your brother and ask him for help in creating this trip as a vision quest."

"Harry? What would he know about my situation?" he said with contempt.

"You know nothing about your brother! He's one of the finest, most revered teachers of the ancient ways in America. Do you know that people from all over the country seek him out for counsel on the ways of our people? If you really want to heal, make peace with Harry, for he has powerful medicine to help you 'cry for a vision'. Bye, Billy, Ho-Hetchetualoh."

"What does that mean, Jen?"

"Ask Harry," she said out the window as she drove away."

10
CRYING FOR A VISION

Billy figured that if he called Harry first, his brother probably wouldn't want to see him, so he decided to just drop in. Harry and their sister, Angelina, lived together and were both still single. Angelina was a school teacher on the reservation, and was an easy going person who was loved by everyone. Harry was the drummer and percussionist in 'Red Road', and also was respected as a medicine man.

Billy pulled into the gravel driveway, got out of his car and knocked on the door. His sister answered, and after registering a shocked expression, threw her arms around his neck.

"God, it's so good to see you, Billy. I hope nothing's wrong, is it?"

"Everything's fine Angie, where's Harry?"

"He's out in the barn making a new drum, why?"

"I thought it was time that he and I had a talk."

"Billy, please don't start trouble," she said running after him.

"I won't Angie, I promise."

As Billy walked from the house down the dirt driveway towards the barn, he had flashbacks of their childhood together. Harry was the oldest, then Billy two years his junior, and Angelina was three years younger than Billy. Harry and Angie favored their father, very dark complexions, short, heavy set physiques bordering on over weight, and long, jet black hair usually worn braided.

Billy favored their mother. He was six feet two inches tall, heavily muscled, very athletic and short haired. Personality-wise, Angie was very gentle and easy going, and wonderful with children. Harry was fiercely private and stubborn, yet a patient and thorough purveyor of the ancient Sioux traditions. They wore jeans and buckskin jackets, Billy wore Armani suits. Their lives revolved around cooperative endeavors, Billy's life was based on competitive efforts. Consequently, the brothers were never close, but Angie loved them both.

Harry made no effort to hide his contempt for Billy's decision to ignore their family traditions. Billy thought of Harry as a reservation hick whose life would never amount to much. They were as different as night and day, and other than growing up in the same house, were not part of each others lives.

Billy walked to the entrance of the barn and saw Harry attaching an animal skin onto a hollowed out tree trunk which would eventually be a drum. Billy called out, "Hey, big brother, how's the drum coming?"

Harry turned around to see Billy standing there, and resumed his work. "Not even a hello for your brother?"

"My brother is dead to me."

"Wow, Harry, is it really that bad between us?" The drummer just kept working without any acknowledgment of his brother's words.

"Harry, I need to talk to you."

"We have nothing to talk about."

"Harry, I've been a jerk to you and to Mom and Dad and I now realize that. I've hit the wall in my life, and I know that the part of me that needs fame and fortune is dying. So you're right, I am dead. I always lived my life thinking I could out-run, out-think, and out-do everyone. It was always I, me, mine. That thinking has gotten me into a very dark place in my life. I'm losing in court, and I'm losing Jenny. I don't know how to get off the treadmill of what my life has become, but I can't keep living like this. Grandma and Jenny both suggested I go to Broken Rock Mountain to clear my head. Jen also said that a vision quest would help me to get on the right track. Problem is, I don't know what one is, how to do it, or where to start. She said that you are the man to help me, and I thought this would be a great opportunity for us to begin our relationship all over again." Harry stared off into space, then shook his head slowly.

"Do you think you can just walk in here and dump your problems on me and that will make up for a lifetime of ignorance? I haven't seen you in years. Why should I help you?"

Billy stopped and thought for a moment. "Do you remember when we got into a fight over that old fishing pole grandpa made when we were kids?"

"Yeah."

"After you whipped me pretty good for it, Dad broke up the fight and said something I'll never forget. Do you remember?"

"No, I don't."

"He said to me - 'Forgive, but don't forget, Billy. ' I guess that's what I'm asking you to do, Harry. I'm not expecting you to forget my ignorance, but can you forgive me? If so, I would love to jump-start our friendship."

Harry stopped his work to look Billy in the eye. "Hand me that knife." Billy walked over and handed Harry the knife. Harry cut the sinewy strip of skin and put the drum down on a shelf as he stood up. "Follow me."

They walked out of the barn and down towards the creek. For no apparent reason, Harry stopped, and Billy followed suit. "What do you hear?"

"What do you mean, is someone here?" said Billy.

"What do you hear?" Harry repeated slowly.

Billy stopped for a few seconds and said, "I hear nothing." Harry closed his eyes and nodded for a moment.

"Do you see that tree, Billy?" Pointing to a large oak near the creek.

"Yea, I see it."

"There's a squirrel chewing an acorn on the lowest big limb, and some sparrows nesting and singing at the top of the tree. Because it's hot today, the crickets and locusts are really kicking up the rhythm section, too. Do you hear that?"

"Yes, Harry, I hear it now, but what's the point?"

"The point is that there is so much going on that you have missed in life, I don't know if I can teach what you need to learn."

"Harry, please listen. Our people have been put down by White America for hundreds of years. When I saw this as a child, I was committed to breaking that cycle in my lifetime. I was out to prove that Native Americans could contribute in a great way to the mainstream American society as a whole. But I allowed myself to get stuck on the wrong things as being important. I developed this 'big fish in a small pond' mentality, and thought my contribution to my people would be to teach them to forget the old ways and jump on the high-tech, Wall Street bandwagon. You know, bank account, big house, the whole American dream thing. I now see that the reverse is true. I see that our contribution to American society is in preserving the ways of our ancestors. We need to teach this disposable, neurotic society the Indian way of living peacefully in harmony with nature. I lost that ability, and I sure would appreciate learning it from you."

"Your words have power, but talk is cheap, and actions are the only real measure of one's intent. Love is not what you say, love is what you do," was Harry's reply. He turned and walked out to the meadow next to the barn. The younger brother followed. Harry laid down in the middle of the high grass, and Billy laid down nearby. "What do you see?" asked Harry.

This time Billy was really trying to be observant. "I see the sky, the clouds, the sun, and the grass," he said.

"What do you see in the grass?" the teacher asked.

Billy looked for several minutes before answering. He noticed tiny spiders connecting their webs from blade to blade in the grass. "I see spiders spinning webs in the grass."

"Good. How do they determine which blades of grass they'll move to?"

"I'm not sure," said the student.

"I'll tell you. They jump off the blade they're connected to, jump right up into the wind, and they trust that wherever they land is the perfect place. Do you see the faith they must have to do this? They completely trust the whole process. You, on the other hand, have never trusted me, nor have you trusted anyone that I can remember. I have nothing to teach such a person."

"If I proved my trust in you, would you help me?" They heard someone behind them and looked up to see Angie.

"Please help him, Harry," she said with plaintive eyes. Harry dropped his head down in frustration. Many nervous minutes passed and the air was charged with tension as Billy began walking away dejectedly.

"Wait, Billy." Harry walked over to him and looked into his brother's eyes. "You must respect me, and you must trust me. I'll remove myself from making any decisions about your evolution and allow Great Spirit to teach through me. So the trusting is imperative on all levels, from Spirit to teacher, to student, back to teacher, back to Spirit. Do you understand?"

"Yes."

"Good."

"Harry, I have a question. It's probably a stupid

one."

"The only stupid question is the one you don't ask."

"Couldn't it be that the spider is just a dumb, jumping nervous system? In other words, it may be too dumb to do anything else but jump, and faith and all that has nothing to do with it?"

"Come with me," he started walking in the direction of the creek. Harry looked through the bushes that lined the creek for such a long time that his brother began to lose patience. Then, with a satisfied look, he turned to his younger brother. "Look at this web, Billy." They sat there staring at a web that was two feet square, was incredibly complex and was made up of intricately symmetrical strands of webbing. "Do you think it took intelligence to make this?"

"The easy answer is yes, but it could also be attributed to thousands of years of genetic evolution in spiders," answered the doubting student.

"Good answer! But look further my brother."

Billy liked the fact that Harry referred to him as his brother. Harry was looking at another web site. "Do you see this web?"

"Yes, it doesn't look as well constructed."

"Do you see these globs of thickly piled spider flax?"

"Yes."

"They are put that way to fool the flying insects into thinking a creature is caught in the web. Now see how it appears that there is an incomplete section of the web?"

"Yes," said Billy in wonderment.

"It is built that way so a fly will think the spider is satiated by what looks like a trapped, cocooned bug, and has left the web incomplete for that reason. In reality, there is another more complete, complex web on the other side of the missing section. Do you see it?"

"Yes, I do," said Billy in humility.

"Life is deeper than it appears on the surface, but once we look for the truth, it is always quite simple. You see Billy, the animals are beginning to reach a point in time when they are realizing their individuality. We humans have learned our individuality already, but what we are beginning to see is that on the other side of individuality lies collective oneness. The fact is that we are really one heart, with one mind. We are more than just connected, we are one."

In that moment, the younger brother began to realize that his older brother was an incredibly wise man with fabulously insightful knowledge. "Where did you learn this stuff, Harry?"

"This is the way of our people, Billy. I learned what the elders taught. I have a great respect for all life, and I honor the rhythm and vibration of things. All things have a rhythm and I can sense it in a moment, it is part of what makes me a competent drummer."

"Jenny mentioned that maybe a vision quest would help me get back on track, but I gotta be honest with you, I don't know what the words mean."

"A vision quest is a way in which our people seek guidance from Great Spirit by venturing out into the wilderness to free themselves of whatever blockage is preventing them from acting with purpose and clarity. A vision quest can be one's search for his unique mission. When one has reached a dead end in his life, a vision quest can open up a new avenue to experience. It is a way to get in touch with and achieve the holy purpose that is our very reason for being on Earth."

"Is it a ritual?"

"Yes, in the traditional sense because it is begun by the opening of the pipe. The pipe is a physical representation of our spiritual journey. It acts as a portable altar connecting us to the Great Spirit. Follow me, brother."

They went into the house, up the stairs, into Harry's music room. It was filled with recording equipment, a drum set, many odd drums from different ethnic backgrounds, and Native American artifacts adorned the walls and any empty space. Harry went into a closet and emerged seconds later with two padded leather bags. He very carefully and reverently laid them on a nearby couch and sat down, instructing Billy to pull up a chair. He opened the drawstring at one end of the bag and pulled out a cylindrical object wrapped in red cloth. He laid it down on the couch and meticulously unwrapped the cloth until a beautiful red stone pipe came into full view.

It was in two pieces: the first piece was the long wooden stem that one would draw smoke through; the other piece was a bowl made out of red pipestone and carved in the shape of an eagle. The stem tapered down to where it was meant to be inserted into the side of the bowl for them to become one.

"Grandfather Lonewolf made this for me," said Harry reverently.

"Wow, the old man carved that for you himself?"

"Yes, he gave it to me on my eighteenth birthday,

and then gave me another one on my twenty-first birthday.
He died a month later."

"He gave you two pipes?"

"He told me one was to keep, and one was to hold,"
he said as he reached into the leather bag, pulling out the
other pipe wrapped in white flannel cloth. "Grandfather
made this for you, Billy"

The bowl on Billy's pipe was carved into the shape
of a buffalo. "Man, I just got chills and goose bumps,
Harry. Thank you so much!"

"Don't thank me, thank Grandfather. He's here
now."

Billy got on his knees and thanked his Grandfather,
and Harry knew it was good.

"Billy, let me tell you what we need to do. First you
must pack lightly, all cotton clothes, plenty of water, and no
food. Then we will go to the mountain. We will honor the
four directions in a sacred way and open the pipe, which
means to assign a sacredness to it while honoring our
ancestors, the directions, and Great Spirit. We will fill the
pipe with a mixture of bark and herbs, but we will not
smoke it.

"Then we must do an Inipi, a sweat lodge ceremony.
Water is the lifeblood element in our bodies, and in an Inipi
we sweat our lifeblood until it intermingles with Mother
Earth. In this way, we bond our energy with Mother and
establish a tribal intimacy with nature. After the sweat
lodge, we will smoke the peace pipe. Then you will
proceed on your journey, allowing yourself to be guided by
nature and the spirit guides by closely following your
intuition."

"How do I hear my intuition?"

"When confusion grips your mind, sit down and just follow your breath inward. When thoughts intrude, which they will, just observe them without judging them as good or bad, and re-focus on your breathing. If you can do this, eventually space will appear between your thoughts, and this space is the place where the inner voice of God speaks. This inner voice is your intuition - follow it implicitly."

"How do I differentiate between my ego voice and my intuition?"

"Usually the ego tells you to do what is good for only you, and it says to always take the easy way out. Our intuition, on the other hand, speaks with regard for the highest good of all concerned, and usually whispers for us to take the difficult path instead of the apparently easy path. So listen closely brother, and before you act, sense within yourself what vibration is directing your impending action. If you feel harmonic and at peace with your decision, you can be sure you are listening to your intuition. But if you feel dissonant and unclear, you are probably acting from an ego standpoint, and must instantly reassess your mode of behavior. Do you understand?"

"I don't know, this is a real stretch for me. How can I learn what to do when I'm alone and inexperienced in the wilderness?"

" Knowledge and understanding are always available because, since the beginning of time, God is constantly broadcasting pure love and wisdom at all times."

"How do you know that?"

Harry thought for a moment, and then shifted gears to further explain himself. "If we had a transistor radio, and turned it on right now, could we pick up a radio station?"

"Sure, Harry."

"How does this little black box called a radio play music?" asked the teacher.

"There are radio waves in the air, and when the antenna is properly adjusted, it can pick up the frequency and relay through the radio's speaker whatever is being broadcast on that wave length."

"Show me those waves."

"Well, I can't, Harry. They're invisible - you know that."

"If I understand you correctly, Billy, they're invisible, but because you understand how it works and have experienced it over and over, you know it is true, right?"

"Yes."

"God is broadcasting invisible LOVE vibrations at all times, in all places. When we properly adjust our internal antenna, we can tune in to the supra-physical message that is constantly being transmitted. You see, brother, because I know how it works and have experienced this over and over, I also know it to be true. Does this make sense to you?"

"Wow, Harry, this is awesome," was all Billy could say.

"Yes, Great Spirit is indeed awesome. When you go on your way, I will build a ceremonial fire and I will keep this fire burning until you return. Are you ready?"

"I was born ready!" responded Billy eagerly.

Harry smiled awkwardly, for he knew vision quests rarely unfolded as the participant anticipated. "Go home and prepare for the journey. I will pick you up at sunrise. OK?"

"Thanks so much, Harry. I won't let you down."

"Don't worry about letting me down, don't let yourself down with false expectations."

"Right, Harry." Billy went home, packed his things according to his brother's instructions, and after setting his alarm clock for five a.m., had a dreamless but fitful night's sleep.

At six a.m. Harry was sitting in his brother's driveway beeping from behind the wheel of his old Jeep. Billy hopped in and asked "Where are we going to do the vision quest?"

"I know a place high in the Black Hills that may be good. We'll go there and if the spirits and our intuition approve, we'll stay. If not, we'll move around until we find the perfect place."

"The Black Hills? That's a three hour drive, isn't it?"

"Probably more like four hours to where I want to go. Don't be attached to time Billy. Let me begin your training in the ways of our people by talking about time ..." Harry began driving, and over the next four hours the elder brother gave his younger brother a crash course in the beautiful principles of their people. He talked about time only as it related to the seasons and shorter periods of time measured by day and night. Harry spoke of a time long ago when braves agreed to meet on a harvest moon, and if either arrived at the meeting place within three days of the full moon, they were on time.

Billy laughed and said, "If I am three minutes late

in court, I am in serious trouble, and in the ways of the Lakota, three days late is still on time."

"This is a good example of why the Native Americans have had serious problems adapting to mainstream society here. Our culture teaches us that true wisdom is to learn your unique purpose on earth and that living it is sacred. Whereas the Washishu society teaches that enlightenment is just the opposite. White society teaches that everyone should go to college, get good grades, be popular and good looking, become either a doctor or lawyer, or marry a doctor or lawyer, get a big house in the suburbs and live happily ever after. The problem is that if everybody does that, we'll have a society of clones. It is in our diversity that we discover how interesting and unusually talented each person is, if they follow their own unique path."

Harry explained how and why Native American principles differed from traditional American principles. Billy asked mostly thoughtful, intelligent questions, and, in this way, the brothers began bonding in an entirely new way.

At nine a.m. they arrived in Rapid City. A half hour later they were in Keystone on their way to Harney Peak, the highest mountain in South Dakota. In the middle of nowhere, Harry turned the Jeep off of Route 244 and began driving along a dried creek bed. The ride was wildly bumpy and harrowing for Billy, who wasn't used to such spontaneity. Harry drove until it seemed as if the Jeep would fall apart. Miles into the wilderness, Harry stopped and jumped out of the Jeep.

"Stay here, Billy," he said, walking out in the

woods. He returned five minutes later and drove the Jeep over and through low lying dead brush until they came up to a small wooden structure with a large pit containing many blackened round rocks from the creek bed laying at the bottom of it.

Harry got out a black tarp and threw it over the roughly made wooden structure. He threw three blankets over the tarp, and taking an ax, began chipping wood off a nearby dead tree.

They made a fire and began heating the rocks. Some of the rocks were so hot they began to glow. Harry instructed Billy to fill the five gallon can with water. Billy mentioned how hungry he was and Harry said food would not be consumed until after the vision quest was over.

Harry tossed Billy some shorts and told him to put them on, and wear nothing else. He then instructed his brother to enter the sweatlodge. As Billy opened the flap of the blanket to enter, he saw a small pit in the center with a bucket of water and a ladle. Billy sat down cross-legged and Harry opened the flap and with a pitchfork, one at a time, brought in three large glowing rocks, carefully dropping them into the pit.

Harry sat down and began singing sacred prayers. It was pitch dark in the sweatlodge except for the glowing red rocks which shimmered with heat. Harry took the ladle and, dipping it into the water, carefully poured it onto the rocks, generating clouds of steam that filled the lodge with heat.

"You are at the crossroads of your life, my brother. To go back to your old life would mean death to you. The only path ahead of you is one of change, as you now know.

You are present in this sacred ritual to pray for a vision. That means to humbly beg Great Spirit for a sign as to your divine purpose. It means you respect the enormous beauty of the universe and seek to deepen your oneness with it. Now speak your intent my brother."

Billy sat quietly not knowing what to say. He was sweating profusely and he felt tongue-tied like he was on stage in front of a crowd, fearful of speaking stupidly.

"You need not feel ashamed my brother. You and I are one - different eggs from the same womb - but we are one. We have no secrets from each other. I love you, I honor your courage in being here before Great Spirit - SPEAK!" Harry urged in a very supportive tone.

"I ... I want to change," Billy said timidly and softly.

"Address Great Spirit with reverence, my brother," whispered Harry.

"Dear Great Spirit, I ask your help. I have become something I don't like." Billy began slowly and softly, but like a boulder rolling downhill gathers momentum, his voice became progressively louder and more confident. "I have lied, I have cheated, I have hurt my family and friends and my wife. Now an important mission has appeared in my life, and I humbly ask for your guidance to make it right. Great Spirit, I can't do it alone. Please work through me to help my people and give me strength to be a man worthy of Jenny's love."

Billy became quiet and they sat in silence for a long time. Billy just stared into the rocks and sweated. After a while, Harry got up and using the pitchfork, brought three more rocks into the lodge. He ladled more water onto them, and the steam billowed throughout the small structure.

Billy began to see dancing faces in the glowing rocks. He saw faces he did not recognize, smiling faces welcoming him with open arms, all dressed in the ancient way, and he told Harry. The older brother said they were their ancestors. He explained that it was Great Spirit answering Billy's prayer by sending the ancestors to help fulfill his purpose. Harry brought in more rocks, and poured water on them again. Billy could barely breathe. He felt his sweat pooling beneath him and he began saying prayers.

He prayed for the Earth. He prayed for the rivers. He prayed for himself. He prayed for his family, for Harry, and he prayed for Jenny. He hummed an old Lakota song softly and though he couldn't remember the words, his brother nodded in silence, knowing it was genuine and good.

Harry arose and brought in more rocks, now twelve glowing rocks in all placed in the center pit of the lodge. Harry poured ladles of water filling the lodge with steam, and it became so hot that Billy almost passed out. Sweat poured into his eyes almost blinding him and the steam glowed reddish orange from the soft light thrown off by the rocks. Billy felt as if he was falling in and out of consciousness and could only stare at the rocks. His head nodded down so that his chin touched his chest, and feeling as if he was falling asleep, he jerked his head up to again look at the rocks.

A strange light was glowing from them, and in this light, Billy could see a charging White Buffalo with a brown skinned Lakota warrior riding on its back. Though the warrior was dressed in the ancient way, Billy instinctively knew it was himself on the Buffalo. He saw himself wearing a deerskin loincloth, a bear claw necklace, and a vest-like shirt made of buffalo hide. On the loincloth was branded a symbol, but he couldn't clearly identify what it was. The buffalo vest had a white feather attached to it. He saw the charging animal rapidly approaching a canyon. The buffalo stopped just before plunging over the precipice, throwing the rider over the edge. Billy saw himself fall but not to his death. Instead, he fell into a broiling river.

As if in a dream, the river scene shifted to a scene of himself standing on a plain before a huge mound of earth like a gently sloping mountain of mostly grass and small rocks. There was a line of rocks that led up the mound, to a lone dead tree which stood in the center of the hill at its peak. Then Billy heard what sounded like a snake, a loud hissing sound. He closed his eyes putting his hands over his ears. He opened his eyes and recognized the sound as Harry poured more water on the rocks. He was back in the lodge!

He relayed the story to Harry as if in a trance. Harry said, "You got the vision my brother. Let's go outside!"

They got up and exited the lodge. Though it was a late summer evening, compared to the intense heat of the Inipi, it was chilly. They toweled off the sweat, and Harry pulled two blankets off the top of the sweatlodge. They wrapped themselves in the blankets and drank water out of a canteen. Harry went to the Jeep and, returning with a bag, motioned for them to sit by the side of the half-dried creek bed.

"Here is your pipe, Billy. You assemble it!" Billy opened the white cloth and inserted the wooden stem into the stone carved buffalo. Harry had prepared the mixture and had already put some into the bowl of the pipe. He had the remainder of the mixture in a small pouch, and pouring some into the palm of his hand, began saying a prayer.

He sprinkled some onto the earth saying "Dear Mother Earth, thank you for birthing this mixture." Then he faced east and threw some of the tobacco eastward saying, "To honor the East, who with each rising sun brings us new experiences, new knowledge, and new opportunity."

He faced north, and sprinkling the mixture said to the North, "To honor the Great White Giant who each winter brings the snow that begins life anew."

He faced west, and offered the mixture westward saying, "To the great West from where our thunder beings, weather and rain sustain us with her life giving water."

Finally, facing south, he made the last offering to the four directions by saying, "And to the power of the South which heals us with warmth and sunlight to grow by - we honor you."

He walked over to the original fire pit and pulled out a small flaming log, holding it to the bowl. "We open my brother's pipe as one of peace, of clear purpose and vision, that we may realize ourselves and all life as one."

They smoked in silence and, when they finished, Harry arose and began refueling the fire. "I will keep the fire burning until your return three days from now, my brother. Hey bro, you okay?"

Billy nodded and stared off towards the setting sun. "Here, catch!" Harry tossed a leather satchel to his brother.

Without inspecting the contents of the leather satchel, Billy
pulled dry clothes out of his backpack, and stuffed the
satchel into his pack. He put on jeans, a green flannel shirt,
laced up his hiking boots, and giving Harry a hug, walked
towards Mt. Harney in silence.

11
LIFE IS NEVER WHAT
IT SEEMS

Billy walked towards the setting sun feeling an incredible sense of peace. When he heard an animal sound, he would stop and try to determine what kind of creature it was. Did that sound mean a warning, or was it a peaceful sound, and from what direction did it emanate. He was discovering new dimensions of himself, and as this thought crossed his mind, he smiled.

The sacred rituals of the sweatlodge and pipe opening had the effect of putting him in an altered state of consciousness. He felt a heightened sense of awareness and sensitivity. He was very clear-minded in his thinking and had no desire to speak. As if in a trance, he was just walking with no clear cut destination other than to find a place to sleep that felt right inside himself.

He decided to stop and see what his inner voice told him. The sun had set and he found a large cottonwood tree to sit against and rest upon. He paused for a moment to see if he could sense what his inner voice was saying about his decision to stop.

He heard nothing. He heard no voice, but he did feel that he should keep moving. Without questioning the feeling, he got up and kept walking. He began thinking to himself, 'What if my intuition is not actually a voice, but just a sense or feeling that dominates your consciousness at the exact right moment?'

He decided to stop again just as he was nearing the foothills of the mountain. He sat on a craggy out-cropping of rock to once again test his new found intuitive power. As Harry had instructed, he followed his breathing inward, trying to center himself. He was trying to sense a feeling that would give him guidance as to whether his stopping at this point was the correct thing to do.

Instead of a definitive feeling, there were thoughts that began to dominate his screen of consciousness. The thoughts troubled him because the first one was, 'What the heck are you doing out here in the middle of nowhere?' Similar follow-up thoughts came in rapid succession. 'You're not a nature-boy, you could get eaten by a grizzly or a cougar.' 'If you had any brains at all, you'd turn around and try to find the Jeep before it gets pitch dark.' Billy began to feel queasy inside as doubt and fear tempered with common sense began to touch off the panic button within him.

He jumped to his feet and nervously looked around trying to remember which way he had come from. He heard a screech far overhead, and looked up into the dimly lit sky to see what looked like an eagle overhead. The eagle screeched again, and Billy felt inside that Harry would interpret this as a message from the eagle-brother. Billy sat down and tried to re-center himself. He focused on what he thought the eagle was trying to tell him. He remembered Harry explaining how to tell the difference between the voice of intuition versus the voice of his ego. Harry had said the intuitive voice speaks for the good of everyone and that the ego speaks for only personal gain. He had also said that intuition usually suggests the difficult path and the ego says to take the easy way out.

Billy reasoned that to follow his intuition or Great Spirit within was to continue the vision quest. To turn around now would certainly be the easiest path, but one actually motivated by cowardice. He decided to continue onward.

He was almost free of the negative thoughts that had gripped him when his ego made a last ditch attempt to derail his mission. The thought was, 'What about using some common sense?' Billy reflected on that and thought, 'I've lived by common sense all my life and where has it gotten me? I want to live a life that is greater than common. I want to live extra-ordinary. That's it! This journey is about developing extraordinary sense, which is exactly what intuition is.'

He looked up at the eagle-brother, but the bird was gone. He said a silent thanks to Great Spirit, and continued walking. He was in the foothills as the last light was leaving the sky. He was walking through low sage brush until he reached a stand of pines that covered the lower region of this side of the mountain. He found a nice soft bunch of fallen pine needles to sleep on.

He laid down and, looking up through the trees, thought how incredibly peaceful he felt. He fell asleep with stars twinkling in a crystal clear sky above him.

A loud thunder clap abruptly awakened him as large raindrops began falling. What started as an intermittent tap, tap, tap of falling raindrops became an incredible downpour. 'Oh great,' he thought, 'now what do I do?' He frantically rummaged through his backpack - he had forgotten rain gear. He listened to the weather report before he left home this morning. They forecasted clear and sunny skies for the next three days. He should've known better than to count on them as being accurate. They're only right half the time anyway. He saw the leather satchel his brother had given him. At the time, he secretly hoped there was food in it. Opening it, the first thing he saw was rain gear. 'Yes, Harry, you are the man!' He quickly donned the rain gear and sat trying to get his bearings. Slowly, a gray light began to dawn as the cold, chilly rain settled into a steady drizzle.

He noticed that the lay of the land was a ridge of land, then a valley, then another ridge, and so-on. He would follow one of the ridges up as high as he could. He walked up a ridge for many hours until it ended at an almost sheer granite rock face. All along the way his thoughts had been simple ones like, 'Why does it have to be raining?' And, 'Just take one step at a time; now would not be a good time to slip and get hurt.' He noticed, with slight dismay, that his habitually developed thought processes were geared toward doubt, fear, and negative thoughts. He made a commitment to himself that every time a negative thought crossed his mind, he would re-word it in a positive way.

Now here he was staring at a sheer rock wall, and negative thoughts were pervading his brain. He caught himself and thought, 'Well, this must be a great opportunity to discover a better way to the top.' Though he was actually in a dangerous position because of wet, loose rock underfoot, he managed to carefully move several hundred yards around the rock face to a break in the granite wall. He was tired and decided to stop for rest. Not long after he stopped, the rain picked up and became a torrential downpour. Rain was teeming down in sheets, and thunder and lightning were all around him. The lightning was so close that, at times, he felt he could reach out and touch it. He thought, 'Is this how it's gonna end for me?' Then upholding his commitment to positivity, he fired an empowering salvo back at his ego. 'I am going to climb this mountain and experience the revelation of a lifetime!'

Where the granite wall ended, a groove in the mountain had allowed vegetation and trees to thrive. The torrential rains let up and became a very steady downpour, and Billy decided to get into those trees and try to find some protection from the elements.

He estimated it to be early afternoon as he trudged through the gloomy day. He was soaked and cold, and was fighting off a mindset of misery. It was very steep terrain and he had to be very careful as run-off rainwater was now pouring down the mountainside.

He came upon a small plateau surrounded by trees

that grew oddly out of the rock. He decided that this would be a perfect place to build a lean-to. One of the trees near him was mostly dead, so he began breaking off branches with his bare hands. His hands were wet, and the skin was tearing easily as he broke off limb after limb. 'Boy, I wish I had a knife or cutting tool,' he thought to himself. 'At this rate, my hands will be cut to ribbons. There must be a better way.'

He looked through the satchel that Harry gave him and wrapped in a piece of buffalo hide was a small hatchet. "Harry, you are too much,' Billy thought to himself.

He worked the rest of the afternoon in the pouring rain and built a lean-to that afforded him some shelter. He decided to stay put until the rain let up, but it continued raining until nightfall. He was exhausted and, with nothing else to do, he fell asleep.

On the second day of his vision quest, he woke up at daybreak and it was still raining, though it had slowed to a sprinkle. All around him rivulets of run-off water rushed by. He climbed out of his lean-to and stretched. The view was majestic. The clouds were low and fog clung to the mountain and surrounding countryside with a strangely mystical splendor. He had the feeling to sit and meditate and, as he did so, it seemed as if the animals were just waking up. Birds, squirrels, and other small creatures were chirping and clucking all around him. He realized how much more aware of life he had become in such a short time period. At that moment, the rain stopped. It became humid and very still. He noticed a break in the clouds and the sun reappeared, lighting the whole countryside with a magnificent golden glow.

Billy could feel hunger gnawing at him, but he put
that thought aside and drank in the warmth of the sunlight.
Looking through his backpack in search of dry clothes, he
discovered everything was soaking wet. He reached in the
satchel and found that the buffalo hide that held Harry's
hatchet was actually a vest-like shirt. Hanging from the one
button on the vest was a lone white feather, and his mind
fought to accept that this was exactly like the vest in his
sweatlodge vision! His mind was reeling as he noticed that
there was only one more item in the satchel. He furiously
reached to the bottom of the bag to pull out a deerskin loin
cloth with a sacred hoop branded on it.   Harry had
explained on their ride to the mountain that the hoop
represented to their people the never-ending circle of life.

As Billy studied the loincloth, an object fell out of it,
and as the object hit the ground, he recognized it as a bear
claw necklace. He stripped naked, letting the sun dry his
soaking wet body, and put on the traditional clothing of his
people. He stood up and felt totally empowered as he wore
the clothes of a Sioux brave. A wolf howled far away, and
Billy answered the wolf with a cry of his own, and laughed
at the sheer joy of it all.

He gathered up his gear and continued his trek up the
mountain. After walking for hours, the sound of rushing
water became louder and louder. He came up to what
probably was the source of the dried creek bed miles
downstream where he and Harry had done the sweatlodge.
Halfway up the mountain where Billy was, it was swollen
with rain and raged with fury down the steep incline. There
was somewhat of a natural path along the edge of the
swollen creek and Billy chose to follow it up. He thought

about what a glorious day it had become, and the only thing that could make it any better would be some food. He kept walking up and up and all he could think about was eating. He remembered Harry saying how important it was to fast during a vision quest, but he couldn't help it. He was really hungry. After an hour more of thinking about it, he was starving! He stopped to drink water and wondered why he had vowed to his brother to not eat. Harry had told him that during a fast, if one does so for spiritual enlightenment, the alchemy of the body shifts to a higher vibrational frequency. Temporarily satisfied with this answer, Billy continued upward. He rounded a sharp bend in the creek and found a huge patch of blueberries. He reached for them but froze for a moment. He shouldn't break his word to Harry, or should he? He remembered saying to his brother, 'I won't let you down Harry.' His brother's reply was, 'Don't let yourself down.' If this journey was really about his own personal evolution, then how could fueling his body be wrong? With that reasoning, he proceeded to stuff several blueberries into his mouth. Man, did they taste good. The blueberry patch was huge, and as he was in the middle of completely pigging out, he heard a disturbance in the bushes ten yards away. It was a grizzly bear cub and it looked so cute, but Billy knew where there was a cub, a mother would be close by. He felt danger and instantly turned to run. As he spun around, there was a huge grizzly coming right at him, snarling with bad intent. He ran in a state of total panic up the edge of the creek with the grizzly making up the distance between them easily and quickly. As the bear closed in for the kill, Billy slipped and fell into the raging, swollen creek. He was quickly swept downstream and was

being tossed into rocks and logs. Though he was spared
death at the fangs of a protective mother bear, his new life
threat was drowning or being knocked unconscious by a
rock as he tumbled down. The raging run-off reached a
point where it forked off into two directions, and he was
forced down the fiercer fork which was not the one he had
been walking beside.

He tumbled over and over, swallowing mouthfuls of
water, barely able to breathe, until the rapids funneled into
a chute which was actually a waterfall. He became
separated from his backpack and, though he was out of
control, his mind flashed to the vision he saw in his
sweatlodge. He had been thrown by the white buffalo over
the cliff, not to his death, but into a raging river. He
snapped back to the reality of the moment and saw a low
lying tree branch, knowing he would be able to grab it
before he went over the waterfall. He thought how
wonderful Great Spirit was to have positioned this limb in
the perfect place to save his life. After all that had
happened already, he actually wasn't surprised by his good
fortune. In fact, he expected it. What he didn't expect was
that the branch would break, which it did, and he went
tumbling over the waterfall.

* * *

Life is never what it seems, is it? A simple journey
to commune with nature had turned into a struggle to stay
alive. Luckily, Billy fell down the twenty-five foot
waterfall landing in between three huge boulders which, had
he hit any one of them, would've meant certain death.

Despite that bit of good fortune, the impact of his body on the surface of the water knocked him into a state of semi-consciousness, and it took great effort to keep his head above water.

The action of the waterfall had created a swirling, vortex-like pool at the base of the falls and some debris became trapped there.

The biggest piece of debris was a small tree that must have washed into the creek during the rainstorm the previous day. Billy managed to weakly swim to it, and the force of his grabbing the log and hoisting himself onto it, freed it from the pull of the swirling pool. He wanted to get out of the water, but the sides of the creek were mostly sheer rock face, and he was unable to scale them. He was sucked into another series of rapids, and was too weak to get out of the water before going through them. After the rapids, he went down a harrowing series of natural flumes and chutes where he was banged around badly, suffering a sprained, if not broken, wrist. He was separated from the log and lost consciousness until he found himself washed upon a flat, shallow section of rock.

He was in completely different terrain now, reminiscent of the landscape he had gone through upon entering the foothills of the mountain. He was so weak that he just laid in the shallow water until he could gather enough strength to move. As he laid there, he surveyed the surrounding area. The most prominent feature was an oddly shaped grassy mound a small distance away. What he saw at the top of the huge grassy hill had such an effect on Billy that it was enough to make him stagger up out of the creek.

He saw a lone, dead tree at the top of the hill. There was

a line of rocks leading up the side of the hill to the top that ended at the tree.

It was the exact scene from his vision in the sweatlodge! He sat there drenched, lacerated, and he began to cry. This wasn't just a 'tears rolling down the face in silence' cry, It was a gut-wrenching, sobbing release of a lifetime of doubt.

His mind had difficulty accepting that here he was, dressed in the garb of his ancestors, about to fulfill his destiny as presaged in sacred ritual. If anyone had tried to share this kind of story with him, only a week before, he would have scoffed at them. But it was true, and now his whole belief system about the workings of the universe had been irrevocably altered.

In his heart, he knew he was meant to say a prayer to Great Spirit. He wanted to say something eloquent, but his weariness and emotional state left him drained, so he kept it short and sweet. "Dear Great Spirit, thank you - thank you for loving me and helping me. My life is yours. Amen." He wished he knew some Indian words of gratitude, but he knew none. He decided that when he got home, he would study the language of his people.

What was the significance of this place? He felt like he was standing on the edge of holy ground. As he limped slowly towards the hill nearing the beginning of the rock fence, he felt wisps of wind whipping around him. He had the feeling that he was not alone. As he got nearer to the hill, the energy intensified. He knew he was on holy ground. Then a knowingness filtered into his mind -- he was on an ancient burial ground of his ancestors! He knew that the rock fence was built as a path to walk upon so that no foot trod upon the graves of the ancestors.

He slowly and reverently made his way up the hill walking as closely as possible to the rocks. Old arrowheads and spearheads, broken pottery and other artifacts lay strewn about. He was halfway up the hill and the sun was high at his back. The hunger had subsided and was now replaced with an adrenal rush that energized him with a natural high. The wisps of wind swirled oddly around him and he was visualizing his ancestors dancing for joy with him. He was almost to the top of the hill as he heard the old tree creaking in the wind. He knew something of great importance was about to happen, and he felt more alive than ever before. He was only a few paces away from the tree as the whole panorama unfolded before him. He realized that Mt. Harney must have been volcanically active eons ago. This burial ground had been built with ash and dirt from the crater that had gone dormant for thousands of years after the last eruption. He was at the low end of the crater which was accessible only by the creek, and probably would have been impossible to reach had it not rained. That twenty-five foot waterfall was the impasse, and the flood allowed him to be carried to his destiny. He thought about the incredible synchronistic events that had to occur for him to be standing where he was.

The tree was huge, though it did not look so from his original vantage point. It was so old that most of it felt stone-like, as if it was fossilized. He threw himself against it and hugged it, then slumped down and rested. He just sat, basking in the sun and reveling in the fullness of the moment. The expanse and majesty before him inspired him

to rise up to his feet and scream - Ayeeee - Ow- Ow - Ow!
He repeated this scream four or five times. It felt so
incredibly freeing, he just had to do it again. This time, as
he screamed his chant, thunder rumbled overhead. He
thought of the thunder beings, as Harry called them, and he
watched some gray ominous clouds float in from the west.
　　He was so joyous, he started laughing, and had a
good belly laugh to himself. All the serious events that had
so consumed and worried him just days before, seemed so
silly now. He also was laughing at himself, dressed like an
Indian brave and hugging trees! He turned to face the tree
and rushed up to hug it again. He threw himself at the tree
to hug it, but his chest pushed right into the trunk and a
small section of the old giant gave way and an opening
emerged! He thought to himself, 'Oh-oh, now what have I
done?' Simultaneously, his curiosity was peaked and he
pulled away the rotted wood and peered down into the
center of the tree. A small ray of sunlight was entering the
hollowed out tree from above. Billy looked up and saw
that an old knot about twelve feet up had rotted through,
allowing sunlight to illuminate the inside of the tree a little
bit. He pulled away as much of the wood that was soft
enough to remove and an opening appeared that was large
enough to look into. He tentatively put his head into the
trunk of the tree and spotted something at the bottom. It
looked and smelled pretty disgusting, so he took his head
out and stuck his arm in to try and touch whatever it was.
The contents were cool and slimy and at first he recoiled,
pulling his arm out, wiping his fingers on the grass. 'This
is crazy, what if it's some dead animal that fell into the tree,
was injured and died in there?' But he re-thought it, then

upheld his promise to himself about no longer being automatically negative. He was certain that something very profound was happening, and he was determined to see it through. He reinserted his arm into the tree and reached the slimy mass again, this time feeling small, rock-like objects beneath it. He pulled one of the objects out along with what felt like a piece of string. The string-like object turned out to be an old, mostly rotted leather cord. The stony object was covered in moldy green stuff. He wiped it off on the grass and, to his amazement, what emerged once the mold was removed was a solid gold rock with a sun carved into it! It felt fabulous in his hand as he just dropped it back and forth from hand to hand rubbing it like Aladdin would his lamp. He stuck his hand back in and pulled out six more moldy stones. Each one appeared to be some sort of precious gem with an ancient marking on it. At first, the old Billy thought about how much money they would be worth and that he was probably rich. But the divine being that had emerged over the last couple of days realized that the stones held major cultural and spiritual meaning to his people.

These stones were the answer to his prayers for help. On the red stone, there was a lightning bolt. On the orange stone was what looked like an upside-down V with a line on it. On the golden stone was a sun, on the green stone were three symmetrically wavy lines. On the blue stone, which looked like turquoise, was an arrow pointing up with a line intersecting it. On the indigo blue stone was a circle with an arrow connected to the bottom of the circle pointing downward, and the seventh stone, which was purple, had a circle with a dot in the center.

Billy felt complete as he held them in his hands. A sense of awesome confidence and power swept through him. He inwardly questioned how he would get back to Harry, and the answer came instantly. An inner voice told him to sleep on the hill this night, that tomorrow the creek bed would be empty and he could walk the three miles downstream to where Harry was waiting. Watching the magnificent sunset, Billy found himself physically spent, but mentally alert and energized. The night was warm and clear with a slight wind, and as he fell asleep, he had the feeling of sleeping in the home of his long-lost relatives.

He awoke to the cawing of a crow on a limb of the old tree. It was dawn, and the sun had not yet peeped its head above the edge of the mountain crater. He felt a tinge of sadness knowing that he would never return to this place again. He knelt and thanked the thunder beings, Great Spirit, and his ancestors for all their love and help.

There was no more to say or do, so he carefully walked down the ancient burial hill to the creek, and started the long walk back into the twentieth century.

12
GRANDMOTHER'S
GRADUATION

The whole way home, all Billy and Harry could talk about were the stones. Harry held the red stone the entire journey and commented over and over to Billy about the intensely powerful medicine that emanated from them.

Harry talked about the necessity of deciphering the markings on each stone. He said that the markings and the color of each stone were of great importance as they created a unique vibrational field that empowered the holder in a very specific way. When they understood the message of the stones, each could be used as a manifestation amplifier. That meant that if one was close to reaching a goal, the stone could actually be the difference in the actualization of the objective, providing it was for the greatest good.

The brothers agreed that they needed help and decided that Grandmother Kawaylu and Jenny Raintree were the right people to assist them. They drove back to Sioux City and directly over to Grandmother Kawaylu's house. Angie was there.

"Why are you here, Ang?"

"Grandmother is not well," she said with great tenderness.

"What's wrong with her?"

"It's her time," Angie said softly. "Doc Adams left an hour ago and he can't find anything specifically wrong with her, but she's weak and not eating."

"Make her eat something - she's not gonna die!" said Billy defiantly.

Unexpectedly, they heard a sound at the end of the hall and turned to find Grandmother Kawaylu standing there.

"Did you do your Hanblecheya (vision quest)?" Grandmother said weakly. She was teetering precariously with her cane in her right hand and her left hand on the door jam to her bedroom. She had her old blanket around her shoulders. She wore her long, beautiful white hair down, and for some reason the sight of her hair this way shocked Billy. He had always seen her hair carefully braided, and she looked so small and fragile. He realized he had created an image of her as an indestructible matriarch. But now his heart was so open and his awareness raised that he could see beyond his old image to the truth. She was a powerfully free spirit in a tired old body, and she was very close to going home.

They all rushed to her side, but Billy was the first to

reach her. He wanted to pick her up and carry her back to bed like a baby, but he instinctively knew she would be uncomfortable with him doing that - and his wrist hurt so much he didn't want to chance dropping her.

"Grandmother, please get back in bed."

"Wait, Angel," Grandmother replied.

"Wilson, look at me," she continued. She took Billy's face in both her hands, peering directly into his eyes. Had she done this before, he would have averted her direct stare, as her eyes were so powerful. Now, he gently held her gaze, and after thirty or forty seconds, both began a simultaneous slight smile, which blossomed into a broad grin culminating with a big hug.

"Man, this stuff works, doesn't it boys? I can feel Wakan Tanka coursing through you like wildfire, Wilson. You're good, Harry, you're real good," she said to Harry pinching his cheek. "All right, we've work to do. Angel, please make us some tea with honey."

"Wait a minute," said Billy looking at Harry with a serious glance. Harry just shrugged and sat down in the old rocker. "We haven't told you anything, what do you mean there's work to do?"

"You have the look of God in your eyes, Wilson. Your eyes are clear and your energy is centered. You cried for a vision and were man enough to receive it. By the bruises and cuts on your hands and face I can tell it didn't come easy, either. The last time I saw you and Harry with that kind of excitement in your eyes was when you were kids and caught your first bullfrog. So I know something good happened. Now make tea and let's go out to the stump so you can tell us all about it and we can sit on it together."

Billy looked at Harry and smiled.

"I'll call Jenny," said Harry going over to the phone.

It was a Saturday afternoon at about five o'clock, and Jenny was home. Sensing the urgency in Harry's voice, she came over immediately. In a half hour, they were assembled together at the stump.

The transformation that had taken place in her grandmother amazed Angie. Moments before her brothers had arrived, Grandmother looked as if she was about to die. Her eyes were dull and the whites yellowed. Her old brown skin was hanging and had taken on a whitish pallor. She was barely speaking and her whole body looked as if it had shriveled up.

Now, an hour later, she sat before Angie looking and acting like a totally different person. Grandmother sat upon her stump with an erect back. Her gestures were strong and forceful, and there was a fire back in her eyes. Angie had braided Grandmother's hair, and while her voice was a little weaker and courser than usual, her tone still radiated with powerful spiritual clarity. Angie was concerned, but very much relieved. Jenny was the last to arrive, and she found the others sitting in the grass in the backyard at their Grandmother's feet.

"Come, Jenny-girl, come join us - something wonderful has happened," said Grandmother. "Wilson, tell your story."

"Before you begin Billy, I brought my tape recorder so we can document some of this information."

"Good thinking. O.K. Wilson, go ahead."

Billy recanted the events of the previous four days. He spoke of going to Harry for help, their drive to the wilderness with his brother tutoring him the whole way, the sweatlodge ceremony and the sacred pipe ceremony. He related the high points of his vision quest; testing his intuition, overcoming his fear, being pounded by rain. He told them of his face-to-face grizzly bear encounter leading to being swept down river. Then waking up at the foot of the ancient burial mound, and finally finding the stones. Billy retold the whole story with great passion and humor, though the others could imagine how truly terrifying some of the events must have been. He looked around at each person as a good storyteller would, without focusing on Jenny more than the others. Jenny noticed this and, though it was a small detail, it had an impact on her. Billy concluded his story with Harry's description of the stones as a "manifestation amplifier."

Jenny and Angie listened intently and were wide-eyed as they all held the stones and felt their energy. Grandmother simply nodded and smiled, and when Billy became silent, she spoke.

"My grandfather told a story to me once that was handed down over the generations. My generation decided there was no basis of fact to the story so it is no longer handed down. You see, my generation had a power struggle between one group of elders who wanted to faithfully preserve all our traditions and the other group who wanted to bury all stories of mysticism and magic that included paranormal activity. This group's intent was to try to mainstream our culture within the framework of traditional European-American society. This group had powerful influence with the elders, and this story was one that got lost in the power struggle. It is the story of the Wakan-Inyan - the stones of God."

"Many moons ago, our people were at a crossroads time period in their spiritual evolution, much as we are now all over the planet Earth. A chosen child was born on the day the White Buffalo reappeared, and this child's sole purpose here was to unite all the nations. He was born with full knowledge of his mission, but the density of the energy field on earth was so thick with fear, Great Spirit decided to give him a gift in the form of sacred tools. These sacred tools were called the "Wakan-Inyan," and once this great medicine man had harnessed the power of the stones, he successfully united all the nations."

"Wilson has done something of monumental importance, for he has found the Wakan-Inyan, and with them, you will proceed with fulfilling your sacred missions, uniting the Rainbow Tribe." As Grandmother said this, she slowly pointed at each of them.

"What do the markings on the stones mean, Grandmother?" asked Jenny.

"That is what we came together to figure out, Jenny-girl. While we waited for you to come, I held each one and meditated on it and they spoke to me. Here is what I know so far."

Grandmother collected all of the stones from the group and put them in a line directly in front of her. "Each color has a different frequency to magnify energy according to the needs and intent of the holder. Each stone's marking represents a direction, and probably sacred teachings, though I'm not sure what they are."

"But Grandmother, there are four directions, not

seven."

"In the classical sense there are four directions, Harry - North, South, East and West. However, in reality there are seven directions, including up, down, and center. Observe; each marking is an energy symbol and a direction."

The stones were assembled with the red stone at the bottom, and the purple stone at the top. The colors of the stones were red, orange, gold, green, blue, indigo, and purple. Grandmother began by explaining the red stone.

"The stone is red - the energy of passion, and it has a lightning bolt on it. When lightning struck earth, biological life began and this stone represents the beginning, and it is an earth element. It's direction is north."

"Orange is the energy of balance, it has a warmth to it which represents the south where warmth comes from. Balance is the key to achieving inner peace."

"Yellow is the energy of power, specifically tapping in to one's own personal power through connecting with universal abundance. Yellow is sun, the power supply of earth representing the east where the sun rises each day."

"Green is the healing color, which signifies change. When healing is necessary, change is imperative. The markings represent wind - the symbolic winds of change. Winds come from the west, which is the direction that this stone represents."

"Blue connects with the energy of communication and judgment. Blue represents the sky, which is up, the direction of this stone. No matter what happens below the clouds, the sky is always blue above the clouds. The sun is always shining and it is always clear there, clarity is a constant. It is symbolic of the way we should relate and communicate to teach other, with clarity as the concept that stands out above all."

"The color Indigo compels us to see beyond the physical to the spiritual. It prompts us to see with divine eyes, what has been called the third eye in other traditions. The direction it represents is down. Why down? Because we must look beneath the surface of things to truly see the deeper meaning for true understanding."

Billy raised his hand. She nodded at him to speak. "I don't understand what this means, Grandmother. Can you explain further?"

She thought for a moment, then spoke. "Most people come upon the ocean and only see a big body of water, and how that water directly affects their physical desires. They say, 'Oh, water. I'm thirsty, let me drink, or I'm hungry, let me fish, etc.' There is nothing wrong with this, but looking with divine eyes we see beneath the surface, where there is so much more. We understand there is a whole universe underneath the surface."

"There are dolphins, which communicate with sound and thought as do the whales. There are sharks which are the grizzly of the ocean. If a shark kills, it only does so to survive, but seeing it divinely, thousands of other ocean creatures are fed when the shark kills. There are millions of plants, animals, microscopic life and so on. Only looking at the surface, one misses so much. The direction down teaches us to see beneath the surface. Do you see what I mean, Wilson?"

"Yes, thank you Grandmother."

Jenny was impressed that Billy had raised his hand

instead of just interrupting as he probably would have only days before. She could sense a sincerity for learning the truly important things, and felt a warmth for him inside that caught her unexpectedly. At that very moment, Billy beamed that boyish smile at her that she had fallen in love with years ago, and she felt herself blush.

"Purple is the direction of the center. It connects to the energy of spiritual pursuits. Spirituality comes from centeredness, its true test is within us, and how we live and act upon what is within. Being centered means being connected and acting in unison with the Great Spirit within." Grandmother finished with this sentence.

Jenny had been silent the whole time, and now was eager to speak. "That was truly a beautiful explanation, Grandmother. I think these stones have appeared in Billy's life right now to help him with the trial."

"It is much more than that, Jenny-girl," said Grandmother. "These stones represent a bridge between the past golden age that occurred here thousands of years ago, and the problems the planet currently faces. Once the stones are deciphered, the teachings they symbolize will help guide us in re-establishing an age of unity and harmony unprecedented in written history."

"How can we decipher their meaning?" asked Billy.

Grandmother shook her head back and forth in silence as if she didn't know, when Harry suddenly got up and walked out towards the front yard. Everyone looked at Billy as if he may know where his brother was going. He shrugged his shoulders as if to say he didn't know either. A minute later Harry came back with his back pack. He sat down in the circle again and looked at Grandmother.

"I think we should smoke."

He handed the pipe to Grandmother, but she pushed it back to him saying, "This is Wilson's prayer to speak."

Harry put his pipe away, and pulled out Billy's pipe and carefully handed it to his brother to assemble. Billy bowed his head and humbly accepted it with both hands, then opened the white flannel cloth that protected it. When Grandmother saw the red pipestone buffalo carved into the end of the pipe, she gasped.

"What's wrong grandmother?" asked Angie with concern in her voice.

"Your grandfather told me that this pipe was the last one he would ever make."

"So what, Grandma, what's so significant about that?" asked Billy.

"Have you opened the pipe yet?" asked Grandmother, softly.

"Yes," said Harry.

Grandmother nodded and a faint smile came to her face. "Grandfather also told me that it was the last pipe I would ever smoke ..."

They all sat in stunned silence. Billy remembered his grandfather with fond memories. He smelled like old leather and apples, and he always had a story that seemed to deepen the meaning in any situation. What most people sought him out for was his uncanny clairvoyant ability. He was very rarely wrong with his predictions.

"Grandfather was not always right, Grandmother," Harry weakly offered.

She laughed a big hearty laugh, "True, Harry, quite true. The one time I remember him being wrong was when he said you'd shoot a sixteen point buck on opening day of bow-season in ... what year was it, maybe 1969 ..."

"It was 1968, Grandmother."

"Whatever. You came home with a fifteen pointer didn't you?"

Harry nodded glumly.

"Geez, Harry, why the long face, it proved Grandpa wasn't *always* right, which is wonderful, isn't it?"

"Tell them the whole story, Harry," said Grandmother.

"I shot that buck on the side of a hill, and it ran a long way after I shot it. After running almost a mile, it dropped dead. It fell down a ravine, and when I followed the blood trail to where it lay, I saw that as it had fallen, it hit its head against a large rock. I found this laying next to it." Harry lifted a three inch piece of cracked deer antler that he wore attached to a leather necklace. "The buck was actually a sixteen pointer."

"This is crazy, Harry! Grandmother, just don't smoke the pipe!" yelled Billy jumping to his feet.

"Billy, sit down," said Grandmother quietly. Grandmother closed her eyes, and began singing a Sioux chant.

"What does it mean?" asked Billy.

"It means I am not my body, I am Great Spirit in a body. It means I hear the ancestors from the other side, they are calling me home. Even if I don't smoke the pipe, Billy, I am going to die soon. I am not afraid -- I am excited. Only my body will die, not me."

"How can you feel that way about dying?" Billy said unhappily.

"It's more like a graduation," said grandmother. Her words created an uncomfortable feeling that hung in the air around them.

"Let us smoke in celebration of my graduation," she said.

Harry prepared the mixture while Billy assembled the pipe. Harry lit it for his younger brother and they passed it around two times. The consciousness of the group shifted from death to meditation. They sat in silence until dark, when Billy and Harry built a fire together, then they all sat some more.

13
DECIPHERING THE MESSAGE

Grandmother again began singing a song. Harry sat up, somewhat surprised, saying, "What is that song, Grandmother? I've never heard it."

Jenny was shocked to hear him say that, for he was a musician, and he knew all the ancient and modern songs of the Sioux better than anyone in South Dakota. Ignoring Harry, Grandmother kept right on singing and then with her eyes closed, she began babbling unintelligible gibberish.

"Oh man, Harry, Grandma's losing it - we better get her to a hospital right now, I mean NOW," yelled Billy.

"Wait, Harry, something's happening here. I'm not positive, but I think we should just wait a minute," said Jenny.

Grandmother's head nodded down to her chest for a

second, then she began gulping and gasping for air as if she
was breathing for the very first time. Her head popped up
suddenly and in a lilting sing-song voice said, "Hello
children!" It sounds like a completely different person ,
Billy thought to himself. "That's because I am a completely
different person - ha!" said the voice speaking through
Grandmother's body.

Jenny studied her face, and voice inflections. "Are
you channeling your spirit through Grandmother's body
with her permission?"

"Of course my child! To do otherwise is against
natural law! She whom you call the Grandmother meditated
on two things. First, she dearly wants to complete the
translation of the sacred crystals, and second, she wants to
prepare for her journey back to expanded self. Indeed,
these two thoughts are of course connected because she
cannot make her transition until she facilitates the
deciphering of the teachings these stones represent. This
thought opened the doorway for me to enter."

Grandmother's body had taken on a whole different
posture, body-language and energy. Her hand movements
were quick and precise, her syntax and vocal tone were
totally altered - even her face was different.

The group sat almost dazed around her as she
beamed at them all, her eyes half open but appearing to see
nevertheless.

Billy asked, "How did you read my thought about
sounding like a different person, not Grandmother?"

"Beloved master, for me to answer that question
would deny you the full experience of learning to do so
yourself. Do you understand?"

"No," he replied.

"She doesn't want to limit the upcoming exploration of your telepathic abilities, Billy. She would be ripping you off if she explained it," said Jenny. Billy nodded in disbelief.

"Where's Grandmother?" asked Angie.

"Your Grandmother is enjoying a tour of her soon-to-be home. She is finding it to be a wonderful thing traveling in a spirit body - no packing, no gas, just think and go!"

"Harry, what is going on here? Is Grandmother suffering delusions or are we witnessing a mental breakdown or a personality split?"

"Would he who is called Harry mind if I respond to the master's question?" asked the entity.

"Go ahead."

"Dear master, all beings come to your Earth for a very specific reason which we call your earth mission. Each person's earth mission is unique, but the desired end result is always the same - learning to give love and receive love as God does, because God is what you are. The one you call Grandmother has learned this lesson. The only incomplete part of her earth mission has to do with uncovering the teachings of the sacred crystals. Do not be selfish, master. Why should she have to stay after school?"

"Whatdya mean?" Billy stammered.

"Do you remember how Mrs. Young made you stay after school and how you didn't like it?" asked the being.

"Oh, my God, how did she know that?"

"Do you remember how it made you feel, master?"

"Yes. Like I was in jail."

"Indeed. Allow your love of the Grandmother to exceed your selfish desire to have her stay beyond the completion of her earth mission! Do not be fooled into thinking that you understand death. You do not. Death of the body is birth into spirit. It is such a wonderful thing for an old, tired body to feel young and energetic again! Dying is easy - you've done it many times before. It's living that is hard, and because of this fact, there is nothing greater than a life well lived. We, in the spirit world, envy you body-bound spirits. Do you understand, young master?"

Billy was completely blown away by what was happening. His mind reeled trying to find the answers to the many impossible questions that blurred his thoughts. 'Who was this being? How was she reading his current thoughts? How did she know about Mrs. Young? Could she know anything about him that she wanted to know, and if she could, he was probably in for a real good beating.'

"I understand some of what you say, and some things I don't get," he answered honestly.

"What do you not understand?"

"Who are you, first of all?"

"I am known as the Mother. My spirit name is Devi. My name in my last earth mission was Chantisita. In that lifetime, I was the mother of your people. My five sons were the chiefs of the original five tribes in this land. I brought us to this continent to avoid persecution in our ancient country, as did the immigrants who came here over the last three hundred years."

"Did you pillage, infect and kill the original inhabitants when you came, as did the Europeans?" said Harry indignantly.

"No, we did not. Though what was done to the native peoples here was terrible, is holding that memory helping you to move ahead or to stay in inertia?"

"I will never forget what happened to our people or it is destined to happen again!" Harry said forcefully, barely able to contain his anger.

"I am sorry, master. Know that the beings who participated in the transgressions against the natives have suffered greatly for their wrongdoing. Many of them have chosen to incarnate into your tribe specifically for the earth mission of teaching the world the beauty and power of your people's lifestyle. Does what I'm saying resonate with you, master?"

"Yes ... it does." He did not want to let on as to how deeply he was feeling this interaction. Being the brave, spiritual man he was, he pressed on with the dialogue. Then, as this line of thought continued to unfold in his mind, its implications were too much for the older brother.

"Are you saying that I could have been a Washishu in my last lifetime, that I actually might have killed those whom I now call brother?" he said horrified.

"If that were the truth, dear master, do you believe that you have corrected the error in your current life?"

"You have Harry, no one has done more for the Lakota people than you" said Jenny supportively.

"Yes," said Angie.

"No one has done more for the Lakota than you, Harry," responded Billy.

Tears came to Harry's eyes. He began to think how much hatred he still had for those who persecuted his people. "Is ... is it ... true?"

"Do you desire to know master?"

"I *must* know."

At that moment, she lightly touched his forehead between the eyebrows and Harry saw a flash of light followed by a momentary lapse in consciousness. He then opened his eyes to see flashing scenes of life from a different time. He looked at his hands - he was Caucasian, he had a brown beard and wore dirty, worn clothing - he was a farmer. Yes, he loved nature, so he farmed. Now he saw his family and himself persecuted by those with advanced technology and superior weaponry. He saw himself agonize about going to the New World. He decided to go, and moved to the frontier of the New World where the savages occasionally attacked settlers. He felt his hatred towards these savages and how he despised their crude ways. He clutched his musket tightly and mused at their spears and bows, feelings of superiority coursing though his veins. Harry couldn't believe how in that lifetime he failed to realize that he had become the archetype of the oppressor in England that he had run away from.

Embittered by the loss of two children to disease, he ruthlessly killed the Indians, not unlike the way the land barons in England murdered uncooperative farmers. He died bitter and lonely, and death was a blessing for his tortured form. He followed his soul up into expanded self where all hatred peeled away. As expanded self, his soul decided that in order for the greatest learning to occur, he must incarnate as a Native American who would hopefully preserve the legacy of the Sioux. The moment his spirit committed to this 'earth mission,' Harry lapsed into consciousness once again, awakening seconds later back at the fireside.

"I can't believe I had been what I've most despised this time around," Harry said in anguish.

"Let it go, young master. You are so loved, you have done so well. We are exceedingly proud of you. Don't you see the depth of what you have done? Look at how you have evolved towards what Great Spirit is. You have splendidly corrected course and are well on your way to fulfilling your earth mission, and we are so proud of you!"

She held out Grandmother's arms to Harry and they hugged and he cried and cried. They all cried, except the Divine Mother, who lovingly stroked his head and smiled.

"Master, what you were means nothing. What you are means everything! In spirit form between lifetimes you committed to ending suffering and to honoring the ways you had formerly despised. Pick up the red stone." Harry did so. "What does red symbolize?"

Wiping his tears away, he said, "Red is the earth. It symbolizes the tribe, our culture, how we have been brought up to believe the way things should be."

"Very Good, master, you are wise. The lightning bolt represents energy from heaven to earth. It represents the conceptual field of opposites - light/dark, pleasure/pain, happy/sad, that exist only to further the understanding of each. Without darkness, we cannot understand light. If pleasure were a constant, we would become bored. Pain allows us to truly understand pleasure. Never knowing sadness, happiness is impossible to fully know. This is why experiencing Earth allows us to appreciate Heaven. Do you see?"

The group answered a resounding "YES!" almost simultaneously. "The teaching from this sacred crystal concerns the conceptual opposites called right and wrong, about which so many people on Earth are confused.

"Know the difference between right and wrong. Right actions bring suffering to an end, wrong actions create more suffering - that is the teaching of the red crystal."

"The crusades were done under the name of God, which is supposedly right, yet hundreds of thousands were murdered and suffered. To create suffering can never be justified - not in the name of God or for any other reason. It is always wrong! Apply this principle first to your own lives before measuring others by it. Doing so will build your power upon a firm foundation which then, and only then, allows you to share the teaching with others."

"Dear Goddess, please pick up the orange crystal," said the Divine Being to Jenny. "What do you feel or think when you hold this sacred crystal?"

"I know the energy system by the seven energy centers in the physical body called chakras, Mother. Do you know what I'm referring to?"

"Yes, yes, continue."

"Orange is the second chakra, the area which governs sexual and emotional balancing." Jenny held the stone to her heart, then over her abdomen, which is the area the second chakra governs.

"Yes, Goddess, and the symbol on the crystal depicts a scale in balance. It is difficult to tell someone how to live in balance because each being has different likes and dislikes, but the starting point to achieve balance is to rid your life of fear. Until fear is dispelled, it is impossible to align universal energy beyond this chakra. The energy of Earth is such that people automatically fear and doubt, instead of what we're meant to do, which is to love and believe. You are here to learn, so when you fear something, you are saying to your soul, 'I obviously don't understand this thing or I wouldn't fear it, so send me the very experience I fear!' Loving a thing or an experience sends the signal to your soul that a learning has been completed, and the new information is stored in the appropriate chakra. Fearing an experience like cancer, for example, actually creates more of it growing in the body. Loving and accepting cancer as the lesson it truly is, creates a balance, and signals that the lesson is over, which opens the door to remission. The teaching is - Fear is the enemy, Love is the cure. Using this teaching creates balance in this sexual/emotional center. You then become able to connect the sexual life force with true tenderness to create the ultimate god/goddess relationship. Many people are very imbalanced in this area, which is why so many partnerships now end in divorce, or bad feelings. Lovers are reacting from fear first, and love last. Fear of losing their partner, fear of someone more physically attractive stealing them, fear of intimacy, fear of inadequate sexual performance, and so on. Their fear makes them focus on that which they least want, but what we focus on is what manifests!"

"The young master who found the Wakan-Inyan at the ancestral burial mound is currently involved in bringing this teaching more fully into his life. He, though, is very powerfully established in the teaching of the next crystal.

Pick it up, master, if you would be so kind." As Chantisita said this, she bowed her head, gesturing in a sweeping motion with Grandmother's right hand.

"Me?" said Billy.

"Yes, master, you!"

He picked up the yellow stone and tossed it into the air, and catching it deftly, winked at Jenny. She smiled her pretty smile and rolled her eyes.

"This was the first one I found. I have to admit, when I pulled it out of the tree and realized what it was, a feeling of pure power coursed through me."

"Indeed, master, do you know why you felt this way?" she said.

"Because yellow has power?" he guessed.

"Indeed it does, on many levels. One focuses on yellow or the color yellow when they have reached the point of taking full responsibility for every situation and circumstance in their life. This teaching speaks to the energy of aligning one's personal power and, above all, self-respect. Until you respect and love yourself, you cannot fully blossom into ownership of your personal power. Once this is successfully done, the individual can awaken to this awesome thought, 'I create my own reality. ' This thought is so powerful because it signals the end of blaming others for the condition of one's life. Only then can one fully own who they are, and in doing so, ultimate self respect is born. The energy of the last crystal speaks to releasing the past, while this crystal takes it up another level, to live only in the now. Yesterday is history, tomorrow is a mystery, today is a gift which is why it's called the present. Now is all there is, it is a gift. The teaching of this crystal is - Do what has to be done, when it has to be done. It is about discipline, taking responsibility, not procrastinating, for in doing so, we live fully in the now, and we connect to our limitless power of SELF. The word self stands for Spiritual Evolution thru Love and Faith. The young master does display discipline through this principle, and has deepened this energy through his recent vision quest, is it not true, master?"

"Yes. Whenever I have set a goal in my life, I would ask myself, 'How badly do I want this?' If I wanted it badly enough, I would do what had to be done, when it had to be done, and I wouldn't take no for an answer, especially from myself. This seemed to work for me until ... well, probably around the time I started drinking."

He looked over at Jenny and quickly lowered his eyes, averting her return gaze. She continued to look at him until he once again looked up at her. This was significant to her, because it was the first time he owned up to the damage his alcoholism had caused in their lives. Jenny marveled at the way in which this Divine Being brought Billy back into the discussion through acknowledging him.

Angie had been sitting quietly, observing and listening to everything, though much of it remained a mystery to her understanding. For the first time, she felt the urge to speak.

"Why do you address us as 'master' or 'goddess'?" she said.

"Because, goddess, that is what you are. You are Gods and Goddesses in the midst of remembering your true identity. WAKE UP! I can sense inside of you that you are having a transcending experience here. Good! It means your trance is ending. This whole world is in a trance. We have been taught to believe in the opposite of God's truth in almost every facet of life. You are not puny mortals, you are limitless Gods and Goddesses in the process of mastering your body, mind and spirit. That is why I called you master and goddess. Do you see, child?"

"Yes. I do. Thank you, you are a very loving and wonderful teacher."

"As are you, goddess. We have watched you teach the little ones. You are so gentle and kind - a wondrous teacher indeed. Please pick up the green crystal, my dear."

Angie picked up the crystal, holding it with reverence. "Once an individual has connected with its self and established its power, it is time for the great leap of faith. You have done this already, goddess, do you know what I mean?"

All eyes turned to Angie, and she shifted in her cross legged position in the grass. She was not comfortable in the spotlight, or as a leader of adults. She could lead children for their personalities are so pure and undiluted, but typical adult conversation held little value for Angie.

"I don't know what you mean, ma'am."

"My child, you are so firmly established in the teaching of this green crystal that you could teach it, if you only trusted yourself."

"I do trust myself!" Angie said almost defensively.

Billy looked at his sister and thought, next to the word "nice" in the dictionary should be Angie's picture. She had always been the nicest, sweetest person he knew.

"I do trust myself. I just feel more at ease with children than adults. Most adult conversations are about ego, sex, or money, and I don't speak if I don't have something to add to the conversation. Those conversations don't interest me, so I avoid them. Children, on the other hand, have such an open mind, they can easily absorb thoughts without judging whether they are right or wrong."

"Yes, goddess, you do not partake in situations where you cannot positively influence love energy. This is what the teaching of the green crystal is. The symbol on this stone is of the wind, for the winds of change are upon your Earth as never before. This teaching is - Be someone who positively influences all life forms. You hold your tongue with adults because they are not ready for your love, yet the little ones are. When we come to know that we are here to give and receive love, we constantly influence all life with positive energy. You do this, daughter, and we in the spirit world honor you for your commitment to love as the universal synthesizer."

Angie closed her eyes and bowed her head, obviously deeply touched by the words of encouragement.

"The next piece in this teaching is to learn that it is easy to give love to those who are receptive to it, but difficult to love those who seem unwilling to receive it. This teaching says to positively influence all life forms. I will add, especially those who make it difficult to love them. Do so in silence with those who make it hard and love from afar those who make it impossible to love them. Love the rocks, trees, and all creatures as you would love people, for all things are alive and have a consciousness, though different from your own."

"Your culture has honored this for thousands of years and I urge you to share this concept with all who would listen.   Are there any questions, masters?"

"Should we share these teachings with those who probably need them the most, but aren't really interested in learning about them?" asked Billy.

"We must never impress something upon other beings that they are not ready for, though we may feel it is for their highest good. All earth beings will come to a point where pain makes them seek higher learning. This is the time to reveal teachings. Often, our words will teach in a secondary way for actions are the true test of a master, so I suggest always to lead by example. Then, when an aspiring master feels the wisdom through your proper conduct, he will seek verbal explanation when ready for it."

"Why is creation the way it is, having to experience pain, to be born and to die, others killing others and so on? What is the meaning of it all?" asked Harry.

"We - you and I, and that which you call God or Great Spirit - are actually one being. Trillions and trillions of your years ago, we as the one being desired to play a game. So the one Divine Being created a universe, and worlds and stars, and inserted its life force into a variety of living forms. Then, as the game continued throughout that which you call history, the divine beings in these physical life forms decided to make the game even more interesting by taking a vow of forgetfulness when they incarnated. They did so because they knew the game would be more rewarding in this way. So we choose to insert what we really are - pure life force spirit, into a body - forget we are God playing a game, the object of which is to reawaken to the truth while still in the body. In essence, that is winning the game. Not who makes the most money, gains the most possessions, looks the most attractive, dresses the best - though those things can be fun, they can also enslave. Those desires, for the most part, make it more difficult to wake up to the truth. Do you see, divine masters?" she asked with joy.

"We created this all simply because we find it interesting," said Jenny.

"Indeed! Those who kill others make it more difficult for themselves to awaken to the truth. Their suffering becomes multiplied with each fearful, hateful action. They're in so much pain and turmoil, they must inflict how they feel upon others. Do not, however, mourn the killed, for they are fine. Mourn the killers, for they layer that which you call karma upon themselves, making it harder and harder to win the game - which is simply waking up to their own divinity."

"Is that all there is to life?" asked Billy.

"The answer is in your question, master. Life is all that there is!. Before the creation of this universe we, as the one, knew our Godliness in thought, but not in action. We conceived ourselves as God, but had never experienced ourselves as God. To do so, we had to create a world and a universe where this experience was possible. Many beings on earth are enmeshed in learning what God is not, so that they can eventually know what God fully IS. Similar to our discussion of darkness allowing us full appreciation of light, being not-God eventually teaches us full experience of God. This is why Great Spirit does not come down to put an end to the suffering that can seem to pervade this place. Great Spirit loves you too much to intercede in your experience of becoming God. Are there any other questions, masters?"

Harry, Jenny, Billy and Angie sat in stunned silence as wave after wave of revelation, and mind expanding information had pushed their minds and hearts to the outer limits.

"Masters, I sense that you are filled up and the Grandmother's body is also tiring, so I suggest at this point we end. Tomorrow we shall finish the translation. Rest well and go in peace."

With that, Grandmother Kawaylu's chin dropped to her chest, and then she slowly lifted her head up, rubbed her eyes, and smiled at them. She was back.

"Grandmother, are you all right?" asked Angie.

"Yes, yes, but I must rest. Wilson, will you carry me to bed?" He was honored, and sweeping her up in his arms, walked her into the house and put her in bed. She was asleep before her head hit the pillow. The rest of the group sat at the dining room table while Angie made some tea.

"Well, my whole conception of life on earth has changed after tonight," said Billy, finally breaking the silence.

"I've been in some powerful spiritual gatherings, but that was like sitting with the creator of the universe. Every answer was immediate, no hesitation, just pure, undiluted revelation." said Harry.

"I think it would be wise for all of us to just stay here for the night. This way, we can get up, have breakfast, and get the rest of the teachings from Chantisita. Do you think Grandmother would mind?" said Jenny.

"Of course not, she would think it was a good plan and insist you stay," said Angie, serving the tea.

Billy felt his insides churn as he realized that he and Jenny would sleep under the same roof for the first time in seven weeks. He couldn't help but hope that she would be back in his arms again some time soon. He decided not to push anything tonight, because he sensed the ice between them thawing, and intuitively knew that sticking to his new course would be the best way to facilitate their re-union. After finishing his tea, he stood up and stretching, announced that he was going to bed.

"Where do you want me to crash, Ang?" he said.

"Why don't you and Harry sleep on the convertible sofa-bed in the den - it's a queen size bed that hopefully will hold you two," she said with a laugh.

"Jenny and I will sleep upstairs in the spare bedroom. Let's meet for breakfast at eight, then we can finish this, OK?" They agreed and headed off to bed. As Billy turned to go, Jenny reached out and touched his arm.

"Billy, I'm really proud of this change in you. Goodnight, hon." After saying those words, she kissed him on the cheek and bounded up the stairs.

He felt a rush of desire sweep over him, but instead of letting the fire of passion burn out of control, he said out loud, "C'mon Billy-boy, do what has to be done, when it has to be done." He then went into the den, and after waiting until everyone had washed and brushed their teeth, he ran upstairs and took a cold shower.

14
THE POWER OF THE
WAKAN-INYAN

Billy had a hard time falling asleep because of the thoughts running through his head about all that had transpired that evening. The next thing he knew, Angie was waking both he and Harry with cups of coffee for each of them.

"Thanks, Ang. How's Grandma feeling?"

"She got up at the crack of dawn, meditated, and has been listening to the tape recording of yesterday's session." she said.

"Is Jenny up yet?" Billy asked.

"She's in the shower right now."

"Ang, did she say anything about us?"

Angie smiled the smile that women wear when they

have girl-talked a subject in detail, but she would only say, "I think you two will be just fine," as she walked out of the den.

Billy sat up, pulled his shoes on, and took a sip of coffee as Grandma came into the den. She held up some notes she had taken from listening to the tapes.

"What do you think of this, Wilson?"

"Some of it was so deep that it lost me."

"Wash up and come to breakfast so that we can complete this, OK?"

"All right, Gram."

Angie had cut up some apples, oranges, strawberries and pineapple to make a fruit salad and Grandmother revealed where she had gone while the Divine Mother was speaking through her body.

"The last thing I remember, I could hear my voice singing, but I felt that I was moving away from my own voice. As it became more distant, I heard a rushing sound, not unlike the wind rustling through a big pile of leaves. I don't know how to describe what next happened - I guess it was like diving into a lake, except I wasn't diving down, I was diving upward, and imagine warm, liquid light instead of water. It didn't feel wet as we know it, but there was such liquidity to it, such a flow."

"I cannot begin to convey how much love, peace, and exhilaration I was feeling. I looked up at the brilliant light I was moving towards, and I began to wonder about our ancestors ... in a second I was surrounded by many people who at first I didn't recognize. They were hugging me, clapping, jumping for joy. My mother and father were there! I almost didn't recognize them because they looked so young. The second I wondered why I was there, an indigo light ray came out of the brilliant light, and a message formed instantly in my mind as an answer to my question. I was here temporarily for a two-fold purpose. To allow Chantisita to reveal through my earth-body, and to experience my spirit body and upon reuniting with you, explain my journey."

"Once that message took form in my mind, it was revealed that the ancestors had purposefully taken light-forms that resembled their last incarnate body so I would recognize them. This wouldn't have been necessary were I there permanently, but since I was there on a trial basis, they did it for me."

"There was one person I didn't see, but as I thought of it, a green ray of light came around us all, and the ancestors created a space between them where I could see someone surrounded by light holding his arms out to me. It was your grandfather! On earth, I would've cried, but in this place these reunions are commonplace, and realizing this, we flew - and I mean flew - together."

"What happened next was so extraordinary. We hugged, and then he flew me to a place where we were viewing the physical universe. We were in what you would call outer space, except it wasn't stars against a black void. The stars were a myriad of colors, each different, against a brilliant blue background. We were flying towards the Milky Way galaxy, and your grandfather pointed at Earth's sun. I saw it as a brilliant fuschia color. I realized it was a living thing, and the rays it emanated was actually its love for all things in its radiant reach. What we see as sunlight is actually love radiating from a living being that we call the

Sun. We flew past the sun and your grandfather flew us
towards Earth. She was shining emerald green with aqua
blue fog around her that I instinctively knew was her aura,
what we call the atmosphere."

"As we came closer, I saw a brownish gray blemish
on the aqua blue aura, and knew at once it was the hole we
put in the ozone layer. I noticed many light beings working
on healing this wound at many levels. Some were sending
loving messages to presidents and scientists in influential
positions to correct the environmental holocaust we had
begun. Others were doing energy transformation by sending
different light rays and sound frequencies towards the sore
spot like an antiseptic spray of love."

"We continued to approach Earth, and then we were
hovering over North America. It was an incredible light
show. The brightness and color of the light revealed the
level of divinity that permeated each area depending on the
consciousness of the inhabitants, the level of cleanliness or
pollution, and so on. Almost all the major cities had a
brownish gray pallor that energy-wise looked like a TV that
was in between channels. The rivers as they came out of the
cities were almost black, but the further away from the cities
they got, the water became reddish, and then deep red. I
knew that the waterways of Earth are the lifeblood of the
planet - hence the red hue."

"I noticed that as we traveled over deserted
countryside, the colors became clear and vibrant, and shades
of all different tones. Each tone had a different musical
note and for the first time, I realized there had been music
the whole time! It was music like none that I had ever
heard, or could even describe. It was beyond glorious! We

traveled over mountains, and I saw a brilliant purple beacon of color shining over the land like a lighthouse. I looked at your grandfather and he said, 'It's a monastery,' and we laughed."

"The next thing I knew I saw you all, not only physically, but as spiritual light stories. You are so beautiful. I'm so honored to be in your family. You were sitting around this intense white light, and I knew it was Chantisita in my body. Her light is so great and powerful, my body could hardly contain it, which is why I was so wiped out when she left. When I woke up this morning, I felt ten years younger because so much love was left in the wake of her presence within me."

"As your grandfather and I hovered over you before my return to my body, I saw many light beings over, around and amongst you. They turned to your grandfather and I and collectively said, 'Do you now see how often we are with you and how much help we would love to give? We can, only if you allow us to, so please ask ...' I looked at your grandfather who was moving up a shimmering light vortex. I heard the rustling leaves again, and I was asking Wilson to carry me to bed."

Billy turned to Jenny and said, "I guess you've always been right, Jen, we really needn't fear death."

"The message is not only don't fear death, don't fear at all!" said Grandmother.

They sat in silence for a moment, then grandmother began singing the Lakota song again. A moment later, her chin bobbed down to her chest, and then her head shot up, spine erect as she began gulping large breaths of air.

"Hello, Gods and Goddesses, and how might you be on this wondrous day?" she cheerfully asked.

"Fine, Chantisita, and how are you?" asked Harry.

"I am always great!" she whispered gleefully.

"Are we ready to continue - is your machine ready?" asked Chantisita. Angie checked the tape recorder and said, "Yes, ma'am."

"Very well, we will begin today with the blue stone, yes?"

"Yes, mother, I believe we had ended yesterday with your explanation of the green stone."

"Good. Now the blue stone, who has the blue stone?"

"I do," said Jenny.

"What does it feel like to you, what does it mean to you?" asked Chantisita. Jenny closed her eyes and held the stone to her chest. She didn't speak for what seemed like a long time. Billy began to get impatient.

"Are you OK, Jen."

"Indeed master, she is fine, she is only getting in touch with her feelings as they are being influenced by the energy of the stone," said the mother. At last, Jenny spoke.

"I felt that it was of utmost importance to not speak unless I had something relevant to say. I waited for more to come, but nothing did."

"Very good, child. Teaching Five is from the direction up - and like the sky, it is blue. The Goddess could say no more other than to speak wisely, for that is the meaning of this stone. Its meaning is very difficult to accurately convey in your language, but the simplest way is to say 'speak wisely and your life will be joyful.'" Then she thought a moment and said, "Another translation could be 'Life works to the extent that you keep your word.' The power of this energy center is to have the utmost kindness and discretion with your words, but to always speak the truth. The power of this message is very subtle. Many people speak incessantly about trivial matters because they have little of real value to say. This leads to exaggerations and gossip, which have become a plague on Earth. This verbal plague weakens the human energy field as to the person's ability to manifest his true will. Therefore, phony or false words weaken the will of the being, and conversely, words of truth develop the will."

"Can you explain what you mean by will?" asked Billy.

"Indeed, master. Recall a time when you have lied recently."

Billy's head instantly dropped down, somewhat ashamed as he recalled lying to Jenny several days before about having a hangover from the binge he was on.

"Master, notice how the power in your energy field dropped significantly as you recalled your untruth? Even your body language signaled this as your head and shoulders drooped thinking of it. I see energy as brightness or dimness, depending on one's truth principle, and your energy had been bright until thinking of your lie, then your energy became dim. Now, your will is the ability to bring your dreams into physical reality. Manifesting your will takes a bright energy field. The inability to realize your dreams is the result of a weakened fifth chakra energy field, but its symptoms are lying, exaggeration, and gossip. Is this clear?" asked Chantisita.

"Yes," said the group.

"Also, master, when you thought of the untruth, I noticed that it had to do with addiction. Addiction is a disease that is common to people who have a weakened fifth energy center. This is because all people want to live their dreams. Dreams of successful business ventures, of artistic pursuits, happy families and relationships, and so on. As their life plays out and they continually leak energy from this area, the pain associated with the stifling of their dreams pushes them to drugs, which mask the pain. At first, they feel better, but it is only a matter of time before addiction becomes as big a problem as the one they were trying to escape. This energy center also contains the ability to judge and discern one's mode of action. So the pollution of this area only serves to further distort a person's perception of the consequences of his action. This is why drug addicts are capable of such reprehensible acts while they are craving more drugs, or under the influence. Do you now understand more fully the consequences of right and improper energy movement in this area?"

"Yes, mother, thank you for the detailed explanation," said Harry.

"Will the stone cure the problem?" asked Billy.

"There are four levels of the Wakan-Inyan's effectiveness. First, let us take someone who is unaddicted, and usually a disciplined and clear-headed person. This individual would be what you would think of as the most successful of the four levels we shall now discuss. These are the people that you would call 'spiritually tuned-in beings.' Assuming they are in a temporary contradiction, and have chosen the blue stone for healing, they would hold the stone to their throat area, looking upward, in the direction of this stone's frequency. They would best be served by praying for guidance, and within moments they would receive clear information as to the most appropriate course of action."

"Our second level concerns someone who has been exposed to the unseen power supply I call spirituality, yet has chosen not to use it regularly out of fear or laziness. They are typically well adjusted, powerful people, whose business successes have actually limited their need to seek spiritual development. They have very high highs, and very low lows in their life. Despite outer appearances, they have an emotional fragility that can be easily exposed if and when success wanes. These people have to hold the stone to their throats, then to their hearts, looking upward, and speaking the prayer for humility and guidance. This would have to be done first thing in the morning, once a day, for three straight days. On the fourth day, it would need to be done twice, both morning and evening, and by evening an unassailable inner peace would be followed by the guidance desired."

"The third level of person is a being who possesses what may be called a 'victim mentality'. This is someone who is weak-willed and extremely prone to addiction. This being can ramble on and on about mundane subjects, often losing the interest of the listener in a very short time. This person often wonders why life is so turmoil-filled, and when he finally realizes it is his own doing, he lacks the discipline necessary to solve the power outage. This person could be helped by the Wakan-Inyan by doing the ritual I previously described three times a day for three straight days. The

problem is that this nature of person cannot stay with a
program like this because of an undisciplined habit-
structure. The other protocol would be to do the ritual twice
a day for seven straight days. This being would then find
his power center re-patterned with the appropriate frequency
to seek further counseling or even the discipline to cure
himself. After twenty-two days of sobriety, he would find
his will and desire to manifest his dreams."

"The fourth level of person usually has no idea why
his life isn't working. He often blames his parents or family
for the condition of his life. Alcoholism, drug-abuse,
overeating, incessant watching of what you call TV are
addictive patterns this person may fall prey to. Criminal
behavior often follows. This person needs to carry the
appropriate stone with him everywhere for one month,
performing the ritual and prayer thrice a day or as often as
possible. The difficult factor at play here is that the ones
who most need exposure to the Wakan-Inyan are the people
who are often too undisciplined to stay with a healing
program. Do you see the contradiction?"

"Yes, we do, mother. Is this the procedure
necessary to heal for only this stone?" asked Jenny.

"No, goddess. Once a person decides which
teaching is necessary, this procedure should be followed to
heal one's energy field according to which of the four levels
they are honest enough to admit they're in. Therefore, it is
appropriate to employ these guidelines when using any and
all the stones. Are there any more questions?" asked the
Divine Mother.

Seeing everyone absorbed with the moment, she
said, "Shall I continue?"

"Please do."

"The sixth stone is indigo in color. Who now holds it?"

Harry held the indigo stone. He held it to his forehead looking down at the earth and said, "I do."

"Go inward master and tell me what you see."

Harry seemed to go into a deep meditation, and after a few minutes his body began a rocking motion. "I know that the ability to truly see what and who we are is in this energy teaching. I see that I have the ability to know all things and to create my life exactly as I want it to be."

"Yes, master, yes. Go on ..."

"I see that this stone represents the Down direction so that we symbolically look deeper into the meaning of each thing. That things are often not what they seem to be as viewed with the physical eyes, and are mainly an illusion when seen that way. When we look down beneath the surface with our divine eyes, we see through the illusion to the real truth. It takes divine sight to truly see."

"Yes master, it takes real eyes to realize."

They all laughed at the apropos play on words. "This is indeed the teaching from the direction down, which is why it has an arrow pointing downward from a circle."

"It may be translated as, 'To Believe is Great, but to know makes it so.' Think back only a week ago master. If I had told you that your upcoming vision quest was to forever shift the evolutionary process on planet Earth, would you have believed me?"

"No way."

"Indeed! But you have done so, master, do you now know it?" asked the Mother.

Billy was having a real problem with this teaching. Harry gave him the stone.

"Hold it up to your forehead." Billy reluctantly did so. "Put your other hand on your heart and repeat after me, Billy. 'I honor the sacred spirit of God within and humbly ask to call my power back.'" Billy meekly repeated the words, sounding very insincere as he did so. "Again, Billy."

"I honor the sacred spirit of God within me and humbly ask to call my power back." This time he said it with more conviction.

"Once more brother," Harry encouraged. Billy said the words quickly and powerfully this time with supreme confidence. "I HONOR THE SACRED SPIRIT OF GOD WITHIN ME AND HUMBLY ASK TO CALL MY POWER BACK!" "I see now!" he yelled. "We are meant to KNOW our own greatness, and only then can we truly create the lives of joy we are meant to have."

"Indeed master - well said!" was Mother's reply. "Belief in a thing may not be strong enough to make it real. Knowingness creates the certainty necessary to transform spirit into matter. Developing this sixth sense, this intuition, allows you to know your Godliness, your ability to have clear vision, your clairvoyance. Is more guidance needed masters?" asked Chantisita.

"I think we're lucky to have the tape recorder for future referencing as we need, but we probably should move on to the seventh stone, mother," replied Jenny.

Everyone else nodded in agreement, and Billy looked at Jenny and rolled his eyes in a good way, not in disbelief. Jenny could sense that he meant to convey his amazement at the power and clarity of this channeled work. She reached out and touched his hand, and he held hers for a moment, then he gently let it go. She admired that he had the strength to face his painful struggle by aspiring to a spiritual solution, breaking through old limiting mindsets that have paralyzed people for millenniums. She realized how much she still loved him, and as she thought this, he turned to face her.

The whole group, including Chantisita, sensed the energy moving between Billy and Jenny, and all eyes were on them. The tender beauty of two lovers re-connecting, silently and invisibly, was a poignant way to punctuate the end of teaching six.

"That, my children, is divine sight," the Mother simply said. "Now, teaching seven. I see it is Jaya who now holds this stone," said Chantisita looking at Billy.

"Why do you call me Jaya, mother?"

"Because it is your divine name, master. In the ancient tongue of our people, it means victory. The victory you now feel as you begin to know who you really are. You are the symbolic defender of the people. Disconnected from your center, you are defeatable. But when you are centered, you are indomitable, you are victory incarnate. This principle is symbolic as we speak about Teaching Seven, which comes from the direction of the center. Words cannot describe this teaching, as they fall woefully short. In a way, the moment we speak of it, the lesson eludes us. I will try to verbalize it this way - 'Surrender and detach, for all is on schedule.' The knowingness of the sixth power center allows us access to the seventh. When you know that all things have purpose and meaning, you let go of your need to manipulate them. You then cross over from the individual I, to the collective I, and the ensuing metamorphosis transforms you from the individual self into the Universal Source. As this transformation occurs, you are bound by no thing or event. This letting go is the birth of your true freedom and power into the life of eternal limitlessness."

"I live in this manner and cannot describe the ecstasy and bliss I always feel. Your attachments are many, and each one is like a hook protruding from your body. Life then resembles an endless gauntlet of hoops that each hook-attachment gets caught on. So you move through life getting snared by this and by that, becoming more stuck, and less free. Of course, being stuck ignites inner turmoil, and freedom is inner peace. When you strip away your attachments, nothing can snag you."

"I don't understand, you mean we shouldn't own anything?" said Billy.

"No, master, own whatever you want that makes you happy. But do not be attached to these things. Humanity has focused its attention on objects of desire for so long that it has connected its sense of self-worth to them. People now value objects more than they value living beings. Own your houses, your cars, your clothes, your money, but never lose sight that these things are meant to serve, not enslave you. Most people are enslaved by their houses, cars, need for acquisition, and consumed by earning enough money to purchase and maintain them."

"If they lose the ability to maintain their acquisitions, they can become so depressed they die, or kill themselves. Own it, but be willing to let it go! Then it can serve you, but not enslave you. In my last Earth incarnation I chose to marry a man I did not love, eventually having to leave my homeland in order to avoid its destruction. The power of this teaching enabled me to do this, though many observers felt sorry for me. I surrendered and detached, knowing all was on schedule. The man I married was reputed to be a ruthless marauder, but within him there was also a loving, gentle side, too. As with all earth-bound spirits, there was light and darkness in his being. I surrendered to God, knowing that divine order is always working. Our five sons became the founders of the five nations, and you are our descendants."

"Before I left that lifetime, I had learned to let no physical thing bind me, or upset me. All fear dissolved, an unshakable peace followed, for in my realm NOTHING ever goes wrong. Does this make sense, masters?"

No one spoke, nor could anyone move. Finally Jenny spoke. "This concept is spoken about in Eastern religions like Buddhism, isn't it?"

"Yes."

"If this knowledge has been here through various teachers like Buddha and Christ, why is the planet still so messed up?" asked Jenny.

"Because you deified the messenger, not the message. Parroting the words of the teachers means nothing. Applying the principles of the teachers means everything. People who can speak like Jesus and Buddha are only actors. The message of Christ was love everyone, and learn to forgive. The message of Buddha was that your body is an illusion, that we are really God. So instead of talking about love and God, we must love people, and forgive them as God would. That then, is living the principles of these two great teachers. Do you see the difference?"

Everyone nodded, and Chantisita knew they had heard enough, that anything more would overflow.

"Have you any questions before I go, masters?"

"Dear Mother, are these stones the only ones that can help us amplify this energy, or can other stones do so?" asked Jenny.

"The color, ritual of purity and markings on each stone are important factors which create the frequency that is necessary to qualify as 'healing', or a vibration that may contain guidance. The Law of Three states that all creative forces on Earth appear as the combination of three distinct energies. In Christianity, the Law of Three is called the trinity of Father, Son and Holy Ghost. The Hindu trinity is Brahma, Vishnu and Shiva. Concerning the Wakan-Inyan, the Law of Three is fulfilled as the color, markings and harmonic frequency created by the purity ritual combined to make a unique healing tool."

"Energy center one must always be red, and energy center seven must always be purple, and all the gradations of color in between that match the rainbow would apply to the chakras two through six. First the color begins the frequency. Then the stone must be purified and harmonized through a sacred cleansing and empowerment ritual. This adds a second harmonic quality to the vibration or the song that the Wakan-Inyan sing. The last factor is the markings, which are ancient symbols that have a primal effect on the genetic encoding of each being. Each symbol represents an element as well as the corresponding energy center. Look at the yellow stone which represents energy center three, or the direction East. There is a sun on it, and the stone is yellow which awakens the sun within the energy body, and connects to the element fire within the physical body. Any stones containing these three factors -- color, ritual, and symbol -- complete the sacred Law of Three. The stone then becomes Wakan-Inyan, a power manifestor."

"What happens if an evil person gets hold of them?" asked Billy.

"Because each stone is programmed to love, evil only turns them off. It is as if sunlight represents love, and darkness represents evil. The Wakan-Inyan awaken and grow only in the sunlight, and simply go to sleep when it is dark. Do you see, masters?"

They all nodded. All questions had been answered.

"I love you my children. You are magnificent. If you ever need our help, only ask. Now go in peace." Grandmother's head slowly nodded down to her chest, and at that moment the cassette tape ended. The click of it turning off startled everyone. The group looked at the tape deck, then back at Grandmother, who had returned into her body. She smiled and stretched, then held out her arms to everyone and they laughed as they all hugged.

15
ALL IS ON SCHEDULE

Grandmother Kawaylu and Jenny chose to team up and transcribe the tapes of the channeling session. Grandmother worked the tape deck, pushing the play and stop buttons, and Jenny typed the text into her computer. Together they collaborated on words that were unintelligible and after a few days, they had finished, then made copies of the sessions for each member of the group.

During the transcription process, Jenny asked Grandmother where her spirit had journeyed during the second day's session. After moving her light to the side so that Chantisita could enter, Grandmother's spirit once again met up with her husband in spirit form. He suggested they stay in the group to hear the Divine Mother's explanation of the last three Wakan-Inyan as the information could be important for Grandmother to hear as well as to later read and transcribe. She marveled at how Chantisita's brilliant aura changed colors as she revealed different teachings. Grandmother also enjoyed seeing the divine guides and angels around each earth-bound member of the group. As one particular member would speak and contribute, their angelic team would huddle around that person sending divine energy in the form of light or sound.

Grandmother and Jenny decided to also make a list of the teachings one by one, including the teaching, color, direction, and sacred symbol.

This one page document served as the cover sheet to the text of the session. Here is what it looked like:

Teaching 1 Know the Difference Between Right & Wrong.
           Right ends suffering, wrong causes suffering.
Direction-NORTH   Color-RED
Symbol-Lightning Bolt

Teaching 2 Fear is the Enemy - Love is the Cure
Direction-SOUTH   Color-ORANGE   Symbol-Scale

Teaching 3 Do What has to be Done, When it has to be
           Done
Direction -EAST   Color-YELLOW   Symbol-Sun

Teaching 4 Be Someone Who Positively Influences All Life
           Forms
Direction - WEST   Color - GREEN   Symbol - Wind

Teaching 5 Life Works to the Extent That You Keep Your
           Word
Direction - UP   Color - BLUE
Symbol - Arrow/Cross

Teaching 6 To Believe Is Great But To Know Makes It So
Direction - DOWN   Color - INDIGO
Symbol - Arrow/Circle

Teaching 7 Surrender and Detach For All Is On Schedule
Direction - CENTER Color - PURPLE
Symbol - Dot in Circle

Angie and Harry chose to team up to create sets of Wakan-Inyan stones to give away as presents or sell to whoever wanted to use them.

They first researched where to purchase the seven different stones according to color and size. Then, to purify the vibration, they let the stones soak in water and sea salt for seven days. Harry, ever the good shaman, designed a sacred ritual for each of the stones to have the proper vibrational energy further programmed into them according to Chantisita's instructions.

Once those two things were done, he and Angie set up shop in the barn so they could both paint the appropriate sacred symbol on each stone. In this manner, the stones were transformed into Wakan-Inyan -- the stones of God.

Billy was probably the most transformed being in the group. He quit drinking, studied the teachings each morning after meditation, and threw himself back into the court case.

Despite immersing himself in his law books for hours to search for precedents, he had not found one that pertained to his case. He was energized remembering that Chantisita called him Jaya, and that she said he was victory incarnate. He felt unbeatable, but how would it manifest?

He called Joe Black Eagle, the head of the Casino Construction Committee, to interview him, and Joe told Billy he would come to Billy's office in an hour.

When Joe arrived, Billy asked him what he remembered of their meeting with the county surveyor sixteen months before. "Joe, didn't the county surveyor pull out the state map, and we staked off the site according to his instructions?"

"Yeah Billy, that's exactly the way I remember it. He also said that his state map was a duplicate of the Federal map. So now that the feds have decided to screw us, isn't the county liable?"

Billy had thought this line of action through, and in the old days, would have sued the County. But, since Teaching One said 'learn right from wrong - right is what ends suffering, and wrong creates it,' he decided against suing. If he did so, the case would be tied up in litigation for years, putting off urgently needed work for the Native Americans who planned to work the construction and casino jobs. Also, he didn't want the surveyor and others to get fired. Many would suffer if he did this, so despite having a winnable case by going that route, he decided it went against Teaching One.

Billy was thinking of these facets of the case when Joe interrupted. "Billy, do you have a trial date yet?"

"Yes, the trial is set for November 24."

"Wow, only a week from tomorrow. Are you prepared with your case yet?"

"I'll be better prepared a week from tomorrow, that I can promise you, my friend. Thanks so much for coming down on such short notice."

"Hey, Billy, you're gonna win this one for the good guys, right brother?" asked Joe with concern.

"We'll win in the long run Joe, I promise." Billy knew he spoke the truth, but he still had no idea how he would present the case. He got up to walk Joe out, and as he returned to his desk, he started to feel unsure of himself. He opened his top desk drawer and pulled out the Wakan-Inyan. He picked up the green stone and holding it over his heart, he spoke, "Oh Great Spirit, please fill my heart with your love. I need your help for I can't do it alone. This or something better now manifests. Thank you. Amen."

The phone rang. "Hello, Raintree Legal Service." It was Jenny.

"Hi Jenny, how was your day?"

"Great Billy, are you busy now or can you be my guest for dinner?"

His heart swelled with anticipation, and nervousness.

"Where do you want to take me, Jen?"

"How about if I cook you a dinner at home tonight," she sweetly said.

"I would love that, I really would."

"It's 5:30 now, how about if we meet at 6:30?"

"Fine, Jen, see you then." Billy left the office immediately, and drove home to take a shower. He could barely contain his anxiety, and kept repeating Teaching Two over and over - Fear is the enemy, Love is the cure; Fear is the enemy, Love is the cure; Fear is the enemy, Love is the cure ...

At 6:33 the doorbell rang and Billy opened the door to see his wife looking more beautiful than he could ever remember. "Now I know why the Mother called you goddess, Jenny. You look radiant this evening, c'mon in."

"Thanks, Billy, you look great too." She remembered back only three weeks before when he had stumbled to the door, clothes disheveled, reeking of booze, bloody and dazed, hardly a shell of the handsome man standing before her. Now his eyes and energy field were clear, he had lost ten pounds and was dressed simply but elegantly. She had to consciously re-center herself to counterbalance the rush of desire that unexpectedly swept over her.

"Here, Jenny, I stopped on the way home to get you something." He ducked around the corner and handed her a dozen long-stemmed white roses. She put down the groceries, her jaw dropped open, her face locked in a stunned expression. She spontaneously threw her arms around Billy and hugged him. He happily hugged her back, but a few seconds later pulled back and said, "Wait, I want you to read the card."

She opened the envelope, pulled the small card out and began reading. It read, "May the white beauty of these flowers symbolize the pure love and respect that I feel for you, my darling. For any hurt I may have caused you, please forgive me. I honor you as a goddess, my friend, and my wife. Love always - Billy."

Tears welled up in her eyes. She slowly moved towards him and drew him close to her. She put her arms around his neck and slowly and tenderly kissed his cheek. They just hugged for a few minutes, until finally Billy kissed her lips, at first tenderly, then passionately.

"I love you, sweetheart."

"I love you, too, handsome," she giggled back.

They stopped and stared at each other for an awkward moment. Then Jenny gave him a quick kiss and moved over to the groceries and began unloading them onto the kitchen table. "This place sure looks a lot cleaner than the last time I was here, Billy. Did you hire a maid?"

"Naw, I decided to break down and clean it myself. I even repaired that broken step on the back staircase."

"Good for you Billy. So, how does the case look?" He filled her in on his progress, or lack of it, in finding a way to attack the government's claim. As they discussed the case, Jenny prepared Billy's favorite dinner - roast chicken, mashed potatoes and a Caesar salad. Their conversation was light and effortless, and they often flirted and caught each other just staring.

As the dinner cooked, Jenny was absorbed in trying to help Billy uncover some angle of the case he may have overlooked. "The 1887 treaty gave the Sioux sovereign rights to this land, right Billy?"

"Yes."

"Then at some point after that the map used by the county surveyor was made, right?"

"Yes. In the spring of 1947, the dam was completed, which changed the course and depth of the river. In October of that year, the current map was adopted as the official document in any legal issue and copies were filed in Pierre, and in Washington, D.C."

"Then what's the problem, Billy? Case closed - we win."

"It would appear that way, but then in 1978 there was a big uprising on the Rosebud reservation, and the elders hired an expensive Washishu lawyer to have a new law passed regarding South Dakota reservations. After a big legal battle, this law was passed in 1979. It's called the "Reversion Act." It states that all treaties made between the Sioux and the U.S. government between 1885 and 1939 revert back to the terms of those original treaties. This was needed because the government had reneged on 18 treaties in that time span, and the tribes greatly benefitted in a variety of ways from the passing of this law. The passing of this new law now means that the 1887 map officially supersedes the map we used to stake off the property by the county surveyor," he concluded.

"Can't we sue the county?"

"Yea, and we'd probably win, but it would take five to seven years and many people would suffer needlessly. I believe doing that would be in direct contradiction with the lesson of Teaching One."

She thought for a moment, and then said, "You're right, it would. I am proud that you have so readily implemented the teachings into your day-to-day life, Billy. It's great."

"Thanks. So here's the rest of the story. The lawyer that represented the federal government against the passing of this law in 1979 was a guy named Mason Williams. He was a lawyer who had political aspirations, and was given this case with the mandate that if he won, he would enter into the fast lane in Beltway politics."

"How do you know all this?"

"Do you remember Robbie Biaggio?"

"Didn't he play with you at Nebraska the year you guys won the Orange Bowl?"

"Yep. Robbie the Robber picked off two passes in that game to preserve the victory. Anyway, he's a lobbyist big shot in Washington now. We stay in touch, and he gave me the story about Williams. The government sends Williams here saying, 'Don't lose this case or else!' He loses, and is never heard of again in Washington. He goes on a bender, loses his license to practice law, eventually landing a job as a suit with the Conservation Department.

As partial punishment, he's given a post out in the boondocks, and as fate may have it, the beautiful state of South Dakota falls under his jurisdiction."

"Let me do the rest," Jenny interjected. "He still has it out for any Native American issue, so he hears of our casino plans, snoops around until he finds this loophole to use in exacting his revenge."

"Bingo. The minute he heard of our casino, he probably instantly thought of how to screw us, because no one knew more about this 'reversion law' than he did - he argued the case!"

"Now what do we do?" Jenny said as she cuddled up to Billy on the couch.

"I don't know. Wait - I do know. A kiss might be a good place to start." They began kissing, and a couple of minutes later, she got up off the couch, smiled at him and took him by the hand leading him towards the bedroom. They walked up the stairs, kissing all the way up, and as soon as they walked through the threshold of the bedroom door, the phone rang.

"Don't answer it, not now," Jenny whispered in his ear. As the phone continued to ring, he happened to glance at the caller ID and saw it was Grandmother's phone number.

"Wait a minute Jen, it's Grandma. She never calls." He picked up the phone instantly. "Hello?"

"Billy, it's Harry. Get to the hospital quick. Grandmother's being rushed there as we speak."

"What's wrong with her?" Jenny jumped to her feet putting her hand to her mouth. "No, not Grandma ... No," her voice trailed off. They ran downstairs, jumped into the car, and raced off to the hospital.

Angie was in the waiting room, with tears streaming down her face and, as she saw Billy and Jenny walk through the emergency room door, she ran into their arms. Behind Angie were their parents, who Billy hadn't seen in months. For the first time in his life he sensed how much respect and admiration he had for them for all they were, and all they had done. He had never known it until now, and he wanted to tell them immediately.

He hugged them both and, taking his mother's face in his hands, he tenderly kissed her cheek. He could sense his mother's pain at the thought of losing her mother. "Mama, Grandmother told me she had visited the spirit world and talked to Grandfather. She said that she wanted to join him soon, and to let you know that everything is perfectly as it should be. She was looking forward to this day with happiness."

"Is this my Billy talking or is this a stranger?" his mother wondered aloud.

"It's me, the new me."

"Angie, what happened to her?" said their mother.

"I came home from the store and found her slumped over in her chair," said Angie in a distressed tone. At that moment, a doctor walked up to them and said, "Are you Mrs. Kawaylu's relatives?"

"Yes."

"My name is Dr. Anderson. Please come with me." They followed the doctor into a private room and he said, "Please take a seat. She's barely alive and fading fast. I don't think she's going to live through the night," said the doctor.

"What's wrong with her?" asked Billy.

"We can't find any physical cause for her condition. Old age maybe?"

"Can we be with her?" asked Angie through her tears.

"Of course, follow me." They walked through a maze of corridors to the Intensive Care Unit and saw Grandmother lying unconscious with Harry standing over her with his hands two feet above her body, palms down.

"She's been waiting to say goodbye to all of you before going to join our ancestors. She wouldn't leave without you."

Each person, one by one, knelt next to Grandmother, holding her hand, saying their goodbyes. First Harry, and then Angie. After Angie, Jenny took her hand, sat down on the chair next to the bed and spoke quietly.

"Thank you, Grandmother. You have done so well in this life. All is complete. I'm so excited for you to be back with Grandfather and the others. I know you'll continue the work on the other side and we will do the same here. We love you always, sweet mother - rest. Ho-Hetchetualoh."

Then it was Billy's turn. "Hi, Grandma. I used to believe that when you died, you would go to a good place. With what we've been through together these last three weeks, I now know it. You've always been there for me, and I know you will continue to do so. Go enjoy yourself - you've earned it." He kissed her hand, holding it to his face. Billy's mother took her other hand and kept telling her over and over how much she loved her.

Billy had been entrusted to keep the original Wakan-Inyan he had discovered at the burial ground, and something told him to pull them out. He gently laid the red, orange, and yellow stones over the corresponding energy centers on Grandmother's body. Then he held the purple one, Jenny the indigo stone, Angie the blue stone, and finally Harry held the green stone over her heart. She began to stir, and then weakly opened her eyes.

"Water," she whispered in a weak voice. One at a time, she looked deeply into each one's eyes and just smiled. "Billy ... through that stone," she nodded at the purple stone he was holding over the top of her head. The trial ... that stone is the only way to victory ..." She began to speak unintelligibly, and then fell totally silent. A few minutes later, she sighed an impossibly long breath, and she was gone.

With all the cosmic happenings of the previous couple of weeks, Billy half expected to see her spirit fly off, but he saw no such vision. He did perceive the strong absence of energy. Yes, it was unmistakable. The moment before, her life force energy was clearly present, and after that long breath, only emptiness in its place. He closed his eyes and sat back into a chair. In his mind's eye he saw his Grandfather much younger than he could remember, holding his arms out, then Grandmother flying into his arms, both turned around and smiled at Billy, then flew off into the light.

Realizing her mother had died, Billy's mom began crying. She couldn't picture her life without her mother, and now she was gone. After a couple minutes, he took his mother and father under each arm and walked them out of the room, back to the private room. "Mom and Dad, I want to acknowledge you and thank you for all you've done for me. You are the most wonderful parents anyone could ask for, and I just realized I never told you how much I love you. Thank you both so much ..."

He broke down sobbing and they cried together.

On the way home, he told Jenny about the talk with his parents. He also told her of the vision he had as Grandmother passed. "It was probably just my imagination, wasn't it?"

"Was it? Or could it be that your desire to see more deeply into life allowed you to see what truly occurs during one's transition. Besides, Billy, think about it. The five physical senses govern the five lower chakras in the body. The sixth sense is intuition, right?"

"Woman's intuition?"

"Everyone's intuition! It was coined "woman's intuition' because initially only women had the need to develop this sense. The need arose out of a male-dominated world, where the necessity for 'an edge' against this physical domination forced women to develop their sixth sense first. Now, as the need for both genders to further develop this sense has arisen, both men and women are exploring and developing their intuition."

"That makes sense, Jenny."

"Do you know what the seventh sense is?" she asked.

"No."

"Imagination! This is the sense you were using when

you had the vision of Grandmother flying into Grandfather's arms. Was it your imagination - yes - was it real? Yes!"

He nodded and they drove home and went to sleep.

They buried Grandmother Kawaylu in the tradition of the Sioux. Billy meditated and prayed with the stone Grandmother had told him would lead to victory in the court case. A strategy began to develop in his mind, and the more he reflected on it, the more he knew it was the way to proceed.

As he looked over the legal briefs, he thought how ironic that each official document began - The People of the United States of America vs. the Sioux Indian Nation. He prayed for a time soon that these two factions would end their fight and see themselves as one family united against a common foe: fear and ignorance.

He represented the defense in this case, and as such had the choice of trial by jury, or a non-jury trial decided by the Federal judge. He had thought that a trial by jury would give them the best chance of winning the case, but decided to leave the final decision to the council of elders. Wise Elk was the leader of the council and upon learning that Judge Austin was to preside, chose trial by judge. He had known the Judge as a fair and reputable man for twenty-five years and was confident justice would be served best by him. His defense rested upon the fact that the Sioux Nation followed the proper procedure and if any party is guilty, it is the state and federal governments for not updating the boundaries on the maps. The official charges were illegal construction on federal property, and destruction of federal wetlands, the latter carrying a five hundred thousand dollar fine if found guilty. He also would show that Mason Williams had a private agenda, and that the burden of proof rested on the federal attorney to prove the government's case.

16
THE NEW WORLD

Billy sat staring out the window at the rising sun. Grandmother had made her transition to spirit three days before, and every day since, he had been waking up at four A.M. He would try to fall back to sleep, but realizing he could not, he slipped out of bed without waking Jenny, and decided to meditate. The first morning's meditation was quite fulfilling, but ended with his thoughts running wildly away with him. The past two mornings' meditations were anything but peaceful. The noise of negative thoughts was not being quelled by his attempts at quiet introspection. By the third morning, his anxiety and fear became palpable. Jenny walked out in her bathrobe and said, "Honey, the noise in your head is so loud it woke me up from a sound sleep!"

"It's that obvious, huh?"

"What specifically are you nervous about?"

"I'm afraid of being unprepared. I'm afraid of losing the case. I'm afraid of letting our people down. And that's just scratching the surface," he said shaking his head.

She nodded as if she understood. "Fear. Each statement you made began with the words 'I'm afraid of ...'. Fear cripples, fear paralyzes, fear kills. Remember, you give power to what you focus on. You're focused on fear, therefore, you're strengthening it. Let's first work with the second stone which concerns the fear/love principle. We'll then work with whatever stones may be necessary.

They held the stones to their hearts and faced south. Jenny began singing one note, and as she nodded towards Billy, he intuitively knew she wanted him to join her in toning. After five or ten minutes of toning, she stopped and asked him to repeat after her.

"I create unconditional love in each and every moment of my life. I am love. All fear is gone, and only love is real."

He repeated after Jenny, and they did this process three times. They sat quietly again, and after ten minutes, she could sense a disturbed vibration emanating from him once again. She looked up and he was shaking his head.

"It worked for a little while, but it seems as if I can't control my own thoughts. Man is that frustrating!"

"You mentioned that you still felt unprepared, are you?"

"I don't feel that I'm going into this case with 'an edge,' if that's what you mean. I just haven't been able to uncover any 'ace in the hole', no magic. It just feels like a dead end."

"Is there anything that you could've done that you haven't done?"

"I don't think so. Well, maybe one thing, but it's like looking for a needle in a haystack. I could go to Pierre and look through every case involving the Sioux Nation versus the U.S. Government. We only have four days before the trial, and two of those days are a Saturday and Sunday. By myself, it could take twenty hours or more to read every case looking for some precedent that may help."

"I think it's worth a try. Billy, and I'd be willing to help. We tried teaching two and it partially helped calm your fear. How about teaching three?"

"Do what has to be done when it has to be done. Let's do the ritual, it feels right."

They faced East, holding the yellow stone over their solar plexus and both became absorbed in deep meditation. Time stood still and he could feel peace and balanced energy fill his body and mind.

He knew he needed to look through the computer. It was still early enough to drive to the state records building to be there when it opened at eight A.M. They began the laborious task of searching case by case, and by three in the afternoon, they had found nothing. They were on two different computers, and Billy got up, rubbing his eyes, and sat down next to Jenny. Frustration and fatigue were written all over his face as he asked, "Find anything?"

She shook her head no as she continued to read. A middle-aged clerk who had been watching them work throughout the day came over and asked if she could help.

Billy shook his head and said, "I doubt it." Jenny stopped and told him to explain the case to the clerk to see if she had any ideas. She patiently listened as he summarized the situation, then seemed absorbed in thought for a moment.

"I know nothing about legal matters, but I do remember when the 'Reversion Act' was passed. As far as your case goes, the Act seems to work against you, but why don't you become more familiar with it, to see if it can work for you?"

"That's not a bad idea."

"I wish I could help you more," the clerk said.

"Thanks, we really appreciate your time," said Jenny.

He typed 'Reversion Act' as the key words into the computer, and the computer file came up showing nineteen files. They noticed that the files referred to the actual Reversion Act document and the eighteen treaties it affected.

"Let's just print out the whole thing. It's three-thirty, the building closes at four-thirty, and hopefully we'll have time."

The drive home was a long, silent journey, as he was discouraged at finding nothing, while she read the files the whole way home.

They spent most of Saturday and Sunday immersed in learning all the details of this law and how the treaties were affected. Though it was a good history lesson, they found no "ace in the hole," as Billy had referred to it.

The trial was scheduled for Tuesday at nine a.m., and on Sunday night he decided to call a meeting of the council of elders for Monday. He wanted to get any

possible insights they may have about the case and if
nothing else, he could share with them his defense plan.

He, Jenny, Angie and Harry drove out to the
reservation and met with the elders in the Big Tepee. He
brought his pipe that grandfather had made and they began
the meeting by smoking the sacred pipe.

After they smoked, Billy spoke. "I asked for this
meeting to give you something, and to get something." He
paused for a moment to compose his words. "I give you my
word that I have done all I can to prepare for our victory in
this matter with the government. With your help, and
especially my brother Harry's help, I have learned much.
I feel as if I have returned home by living and honoring in
the ways of our people. I ask forgiveness from any of you
whom I may have wronged in the past. I have recently
learned that a man is only as good as his word. I honor
your trust in me as your representative - know that I have
done all I can to prepare in every way and that I intend to
win for us all. This is my word to you."

Wise Elk was the elder grandfather and he spoke
rarely, but when he did, his words were powerful. "All in
the Five Nations know of your discovery of the Wakan-
Inyan. This is a great victory. Your return to us is a great
victory. All else is as it should be. We are proud of you."
There were no other words.

Tuesday dawned a cold and dreary November day.
The Federal attorney was a man named Michael Shannon,
and he and Mason Williams sat at the table on the side of
the Federal government.

Billy, Joe Black Eagle and Wise Elk sat together on
the side of the Sioux Indian Nation. The courtroom was

overflowing with Sioux people from the different tribes. Oglalas, Santees, Hunkpapas, Minneconjous and others were all present.

The judge was a fair, by-the-book man named Charles Austin. He was ten minutes late, and soon after he arrived, Michael Shannon made his opening statement. His stance as prosecutor was that the Sioux Nation, whether unknowingly or knowingly, broke the law. In the process of breaking the law, federal wetlands were destroyed, and he would prove it beyond a shadow of a doubt.

Billy got up and gave an eloquent opening statement saying that the Sioux Nation followed all laws and codes to the letter - both state and federal. He further stated that this case was truly orchestrated by Mason Williams whose private agenda compelled him to seek revenge against Native Americans.

The opening statements ran until twelve-thirty, when Judge Austin ordered the court to recess for lunch, and to reconvene at two.

After lunch, the government made its case. Shannon called John Epstein to the stand. "Mr. Epstein, please state for the Court your place of employment and job title."

"I work for the Bureau of Land Management as a Federal Surveyor of the North Western Quadrant of the U.S."

"Were you ever contacted by any member or representative of the Sioux Indian Nation with regards to their proposed construction of a gambling casino, hotel and restaurant?" questioned Shannon.

"No, sir."

"Isn't it true that similar Native American casino

projects in other parts of the country contacted you before beginning construction to be POSITIVE of correct boundaries."

"They contacted the governing agents in our office, not me personally, but yes, they consulted our office before building."

"Can you name any of these other projects for the record?"

"Turning Stone Casino in Verona, New York, and Foxwood Casino in Ledyard, Connecticut."

"Other similar Native American projects contacted the Bureau of Land Management to be certain they were not breaking the law, but the defendants did not, isn't that right?" said Shannon pointing at the defense table.

"Objection! He's leading the witness, your honor," said Billy.

"Overruled. You may continue, Mr. Shannon," said Judge Austin.

"I have no further questions for this witness, your honor."

"Your witness, counselor," said the Judge as he looked at Billy.

Billy quickly approached the stand and shot rapid-fire questions at the witness. "Mr. Epstein, are there any casinos owned by other Native American tribes that have contacted your office to verify Federal boundaries in the quadrant that you oversee?"

"No, but ..."

"And is it standard procedure for any company building on property that borders Federal land to contact you in Washington instead of your office in the appropriate state capital?"

"No, but in this case ..."

"Thank you. I have no other questions for this witness, Your Honor."

"You may step down Mr. Epstein," said the Judge.

"Your honor, may I ..."

"Unless Mr. Shannon has any other questions, you may step down, sir," said the Judge.

"Yes, your honor. I would like to ask Mr. Epstein one more question," said Shannon. "In your opinion, did the Sioux Nation err in not being certain of their boundaries before they committed to begin construction."

"Yes, Absolutely."

"Thank you. We have no other questions for this witness, Your Honor."

"You may step down, sir," said the Judge.

"The government calls Mason Williams, Your Honor."

Williams was a tall man with piercing eyes, mostly bald head and spoke with a confident sneer. He was an intelligent man, who knew he was so, hence, an air of conceit pervaded most every word and attitude.

Shannon had Williams on the stand for a long time. They were very well rehearsed, and Williams used his experience as a lawyer to full advantage. Shannon would ask a simple question and Williams would expound in detail with his response. As a former lawyer, he hit home on certain points that specifically countered the defense strategy.

Williams called the Sioux Nation's construction an

"honest mistake". He said that even if the county and state gave incorrect information, it is ultimately the builder's responsibility to be certain of ownership when beginning construction. He very lucidly explained how the "Reversion Act" ceded the property in question back to the Federal government which made building on the land a Federal offense.

Shannon knew the defense would try to use Williams loss of the "Reversion Act" trial against him by saying he had precipitated this situation for revenge. He wisely tried to deflate the revenge theory by directly asking Williams about it.

Williams coolly replied that at the time the loss was a disappointment, but it was almost twenty years ago. He said that he had moved on with a new career that was very fulfilling, and that he barely even remembers that time period in his life. As he testified, he made eye contact with the Judge, spoke softly and patiently, and in general, gave a very good choir boy performance. Together, he and Shannon made a convincing case for the prosecution. The bottom line of Williams' testimony was this: He had no ax to grind with the Sioux Nation, and his job was to serve the citizens of the United States while protecting our precious natural resources. He said he was sorry for the Sioux Nation, but they broke the law and would have to be punished.

Billy thought to himself "Man, this guy is good. I wish we had him on our side".

"I have no further questions for Mr. Williams, Your Honor," said Shannon as he took his seat.

"Would you like to cross-examine this witness, Mr. Raintree?" asked the Judge.

"Yes. Good afternoon, Mr. Williams. How are you today?"

"Fine."

Billy noticed that Williams was trying hard to keep his normal egotistical sneer from returning to his voice. "Sir, have you always felt a love for things having to do with nature?"

"What do you mean? I don't understand."

"Natural things. In your previous testimony you said the Sioux Nation had destroyed precious natural resources that it was your duty to protect. Have you always felt this way?"

"Possibly," said Williams as he stalled trying to figure out Billy's strategy.

Judge Austin intervened. "Mr. Williams, please give a yes or no answer to the question."

"Yes, I've always loved nature."

"Would you consider Native Americans to be 'natural' living people?"

"I guess so."

Billy began asking questions at a quickened pace. "You guess so. In fact, aren't Native Americans the original 'natural people of this continent?"

"Yes."

"If you love natural things, and Native Americans are the original 'natural' people here, why did you try to defeat their treaty rights by representing the government against them in 1979?"

"I had a job to do!" he said, unable to contain the

sneer.

"Objection! He's badgering the witness, Your Honor," said Shannon.

"This line of questioning goes to prove revenge as a motive, Your Honor," said Billy.

"Overruled," said Judge Austin. "I am going to give you limited leeway here, Mr. Raintree. Continue."

"Mr. Williams, if you hadn't discovered the alleged offense committed by the Sioux Nation, would anyone have caught it?"

"I have no idea."

"What was your salary as District Attorney back in 1979, Sir?"

"I don't remember."

Billy walked over to his table and after leafing through a file, found the proper paper and returned to face the witness. "In 1979, you made seventy-two thousand dollars, sir. Do you remember now?"

"If you say so."

"What is your current salary?"

"I make sixty-two thousand five hundred dollars," he said begrudgingly.

"You now make nine thousand five hundred dollars less than you made in 1979?" Billy was trying to rattle him, and it was working. "Were you married in 1979?"

"Yes."

"Are you still married to the same woman?"

"Objection! Where is he going with this pointless line of questions, Your Honor?" shouted Shannon.

"Never mind, Your Honor, I withdraw the question," said Billy, believing he had sufficiently baited

Williams into answering his next question. He turned to face
the back of the courtroom. "Mr. Williams, am I wearing a
gold or silver tie bar on my tie?"

"You're not wearing a tie bar at all," snapped
Williams triumphantly.

"What is the purpose of these questions?" asked the
Judge.

Billy turned to face the Judge. "Mr. Williams was
a highly paid, happily married District Attorney with
political ambitions in 1979. He lost the legal battle of his
life, his wife, and his career all at once because of a case
that involved the Sioux Nation. He makes less money now
and has a memory that's sharp as a tack, yet claims to
remember virtually nothing about that case. He claims to be
defending nature but the record shows that he volunteered to
come from Washington to South Dakota to defeat the
original "natural" people in a case that he believed would
propel him into politics. I say that his testimony and his
track record are contradictory. Mr. Williams forgot nothing
from 1979 and was just waiting to exact revenge against the
Sioux Nation. This is that revenge. Tomorrow, we will
prove to the Court that we followed every protocol and
procedure legally. I have no more questions, Your Honor."

"Mr. Shannon, any further questions for this
witness?"

"Yes, Your Honor."

As Billy sat down, Shannon rose quickly and strode
to the witness stand. "As an agent for the Federal
government, do you believe the Sioux Nation broke the law
by building on Federal land?"

"Yes, sir, I do."

"Thank you. No more questions, Your Honor. The government rests."

"This Court is adjourned until nine a.m. tomorrow morning," said the Judge as he pounded his gavel, then walked out the door to his chambers.

The trial resumed the next day, with the proceedings unfolding in a much less heated fashion. Billy's defense strategy was to put the state and county officials on the stand, hand them the guidelines for construction procedure, and have them read the code aloud. Then he would say, "Is this the manner in which the Sioux Nation acted?"

Each witness answered, "Yes." Each one agreed that all laws and regulations had been followed as they appeared in the guidelines. Every defense witness was cross-examined by Shannon asking the same question. Of each witness, he asked, "Were you aware the Sioux Nation was building on Federal property?" Each witness answered no. He then said thank you and sat down.

By three, the defense rested, and then each side presented its closing arguments. By four thirty, the Court proceedings were over, and most observers in the courtroom believed that Billy had done an excellent job. Judge Austin said that he would review all evidence thoroughly and make a decision as quickly as possible.

The next day was Thursday, and at four, Judge Austin's clerk called to tell Billy the Judge had reached a decision.

At nine Friday morning, all parties reconvened at the Federal Courthouse. "This is a very difficult case ...", Judge Austin began. "It is quite obvious that the Sioux Indian Nation followed the prescribed procedures as it applies to building law and codes. But the law is clear. The Missouri River is Federal property. The high water mark, meaning whatever is the highest point water has reached in recorded modern history, spontaneously determines all land as property of the People of the United States. In 1887, the land in question was under water and mostly remained so until the Oahe Dam was built, which lowered the river level by twenty-five feet. At this point, the Sioux officially owned this land. Then in 1979, the "Reversion Act" was passed, the intent of which was to reinstate many treaties which benefit the Sioux. It has done so up until today. Because of the Act, the map of 1887 is once again the official boundary, which means the Sioux Nation has built upon Federal Land. I have no choice but to uphold the law. For this reason, I find the Sioux Indian Nation guilty on charge one of illegal obstruction of Federal property."

A clamor arose in the courtroom. Billy sat there motionless, just shaking his head. The Judge pounded his gavel several times and shouted, "Order in the Court!" Once silence resumed, he continued his findings.

As to the second charge, which is destruction of Federal Wetlands, I read with great interest the manner in which the site assessment was conducted, and I am greatly impressed with the Nation's sensitivity to the environment. The Native American people have a great history of living in harmony with nature, and the conduct of the Sioux Nation construction crews and architects was impeccable. For this reason, and because it is quite apparent no wrong doing was intended, I find the Sioux Nation not guilty on the second charge."

Once again, the crowd became noisy. As soon as

order was restored, Judge Austin continued.

"Sentencing is as follows:

"The Sioux Indian Nation is ordered to dismantle all devices, building, and construction materials from Tract twenty-seven on the Missouri River within six months from this day. If it is not done within the allotted time, fines will be incurred. As of now, I believe no fines are appropriate. Do you have any comments, Mr. Shannon?"

"No, Sir."

"Do you, Mr. Raintree?"

"No, Your Honor."

"Very well, Court is dismissed."

And it was over.

Wise Elk called a meeting of the council of elders, inviting Billy and his family. After smoking the sacred pipe, Wise Elk spoke. "My son, you have kept your word to us, and we are honored greatly by you. Thank you."

"But, Wise Elk, I lost. We must move everything and begin again."

"Yes, we must move, but you did not lose. We won by having Great Spirit show us we were not building in the correct place. This would have been very bad."

"How do you know this?" asked Billy.

"Because that is what happened. Remember, my son, what does Teaching Seven of the Wakan-Inyan say?"

"Surrender and detach for all is on schedule."

"Yes, I know this to be a great truth. Do you?"

"I will try to see it as you do," said Billy.

"Hold to your truth and see what happens," said Wise Elk. They sat in silence together until Jenny spoke.

"May I say something?" Jenny respectfully asked.

"Yes, my child," said Wise Elk.

"For the past week, I've been reading the printout we got concerning the Reversion Act and the treaties it affected. While it's true we lose the land we built on back to the government, I believe we received a five hundred acre parcel, further up river."

"Do you know what tracts of land are included, Jenny?" asked Joe Black Eagle.

"It appears to be tracts thirty-three to thirty-nine," she said.

"I think I know where that is. It is near the big beaver dam. I remember my grandfather telling me about this area many years ago. He said it was bad because the ground water was polluted."

"There's no industry up there to pollute anything. How can that be?" asked Billy.

"Maybe the salt run-off from the nearby highway polluted it," Jenny said.

"My friends, when one door closes, another surely opens. We will think on this. In the meantime, let us begin dismantling our buildings and prepare for the re-building process," said Wise Elk.

"Where will we get the money?" said Billy.

"Great Spirit will provide. Besides, I have a plan," said the elder.

The next day, Joe Black Eagle went to the new land to perform soil tests to determine the feasibility of building the casino there. Wise Elk, Billy and Jenny went to the bank to apply for a two hundred fifty thousand dollar loan. The president of the local bank, John Brady, received them.

When they discussed the needed loan, John told them he could not meet their request for lack of collateral.

"I know and respect you all, and believe me, I'm on your side in this matter. If you do get the casino built, I know you will pay back the two hundred fifty thousand dollars, but what if it never gets built? How could you make good on that kind of money?"

They sat silently, for no one was sure.

"I will give you a loan for fifty thousand dollars to begin the process of dismantling what you've already done. May I suggest looking for investors?"

Wise Elk spoke. "Thank you for the loan, Mr. Brady. I know we will find a way."

They left the bank, and Billy and Jenny began driving Wise Elk back to the reservation. "Wait, my friends. Let's go to the new land that Jenny talked of," the elder said.

"What the heck, let's go," said Billy. Fortunately, they had yet to get a lot of rain or snow or it would have been impossible to access the property from the bumpy dirt road. They pulled up and saw Joe Black Eagle's pickup truck. Joe ran up to greet them excitedly.

"Wise Elk, Billy, see down there?"

"Yes, it's the beaver dam," said Billy.

"I knew we couldn't build there because teaching five says to honor all life forms, so I came up here, and though the land is situated poorly, it is the only area left that is flat enough to build upon. "I did the perc tests you asked me to do, but the results were so screwy ..."

Just then, Joe was interrupted by the sound of a backhoe making its way down the dirt road towards them.

"Why the backhoe?" said Billy.

"It's the only way to know for sure. Just wait!" Joe said running towards the vehicle. He asked the driver to step down, then began digging. He dug down about five to six feet when a side of the trench gave way and instantly filled with a black gelatinous ooze.

"Oh my God, it's oil!" yelled Billy.

"It's a whole new world," said the elder.

Epilogue

These stories represent examples of people's lives without the Teachings and the benefits that occur in their lives as they use the Teachings.

In Part I, the Shantee people live relatively peaceful lives, yet unrest in the Mocktaw tribe leads to killing which ultimately effects all the tribes adversely. As a result of this, the Shantees adopted an isolation philosophy which meant that as long as their own lives were peaceful, the problems of the other tribes were not their concern.

This mindset is prevalent in today's society as well. Martin Luther King echoed this understanding by saying, "Injustice anywhere is a threat to justice everywhere." Similarly, the Shantee elders realized that the suffering of the Mocktaws must be cured for lasting peace to exist.

When the Teachings and the stones were given to White Buffalo, he had to first learn how to use them in his own life. Only after doing so was he able to bring them to his own people and finally to the other tribes. Let this be a metaphor for your own use of the Teachings. First apply them to yourself and your own situations. As you see them positively enhancing your life, widen that vibration outward to encompass your children, your family, your business, then your community, city, state and ultimately the world.

In Part II, as we watch Billy Raintree's life self-destructing, we may be reminded of similar problems in our own lives. Let's reflect on the way he improved his situation.

Billy took responsibility for his dilemma by seeking a different path than any he had ever taken before. Going on his vision quest represented stepping out into the unknown, where he faced his fears as a commitment to begin his healing journey.

Here is an important question to ask yourself, "What are some areas of discontent in your life that can act as a catalyst for you to look more closely at implementing some or all of the Teachings?"

You now have the same opportunity to increase happiness and success in your life as Billy did in his. Begin with Teaching One and work with this Teaching for seven days. Read it before you go to sleep. Apply it in your daily routine as much as possible. After seven days you will begin to own this Teaching. On the eighth day, begin Teaching Two. Continue this process until you have applied all seven Teachings in your life and repeat this process for the next three months.

After this period of time, the Teachings will become part of your every day routine. You will begin to experience positive results in every phase of life (personal, business, social and spiritual).

You are only ninety days away from experiencing these results in your life. Use the following page which contains a list of the Seven Teachings for a New World. Tear it out, make copies to hang on your wall, or to keep somewhere in front of you at all times as a constant reminder. To further aid you in this process, utilize the two study guides on the following pages. Allow the power of the questions they contain to help you create the life you want for yourself and for your children. Let the Teachings make a difference in your life so you can make a difference in each person's life that you touch. If you wish to share your story of how the Teachings helped you in any way, send us a note, care of White Light Press, P.O. Box 23, Hewlett, N.Y. 11557.

Our wish for you today and always is Health, Happiness, Prosperity, and most importantly, Inner Peace. Please live by the concept of "Give vs. Get". When you Give first, you Get limitlessly. Practice this concept and suggest that someone you care about read this book so they can receive similar value and benefits in their life.

Love, Light and Laughter,
Steve D'Annunzio and Jeff Locker

TEACHINGS FOR A NEW WORLD

Teaching 1 Know the Difference Between Right & Wrong.
Right ends suffering, wrong causes suffering.

Direction-NORTH   Color-RED

Teaching 2 Fear is the Enemy - Love is the Cure
Direction-SOUTH Color-ORANGE

Teaching 3 Do What has to be Done-When it has to be Done

Direction -EAST Color-YELLOW

Teaching 4 Be Someone Who Positively Influences All Life Forms

Direction - WEST Color-GREEN

Teaching 5 Life Works to the Extent That You Keep Your Word

Direction - UP Color-BLUE

Teaching 6 To Believe Is Great But To Know Makes It So
Direction - DOWN Color-INDIGO

Teaching 7 Surrender and Detach For All Is On Schedule
Direction - CENTER Color-PURPLE

TEACHINGS STONES FROM THE BOOK

Now you can have your own personal set of Wakan-Inyan. Each of these seven stones contains the original symbol and color from the direction in the book.

Use them to call forth the Teaching that you want to use each day. By keeping the correlating stone with you all day, you are able to continually access the power and energy of that particular Teaching.

Here is how to order your own personal set:

Name _____

Address _____

Phone _____ Fax _____

Visa/MC Number _____

Expiration Date _____

Signature _____

	Qty	Amount
Seven Teachings Stones with		
drawstring bag $9.95	_____	_____
Shipping/handling ($3.50 per item)		_____
NY/CT residents add appropriate sales tax		_____
Total Amount of Order	_____	$ _____

Mail order to: White Light Press
P.O. Box 23
Hewlett, NY 11557

Phone order: 1-800-956-2537
Fax order: 1-516-791-2177

Teachings for a New World
Study Guide Outline

Many times while reading, you come across a "jewel of wisdom" that you recognize as valuable. In the moment, you commit to remember and implement this "jewel" to enhance your life. You make a mental note to do so, but soon the book is over and that jewel of wisdom is lost, hidden in the closed pages as a distant memory. We wrote these study guides as our commitment to change that pattern and give you a way of maximizing the value of The Teachings.

The idea for Study Guide One was born during the test marketing of the book. We received feedback from parents telling us how much they enjoyed reading it with their young children, or how much value their eleven and twelve year old got from reading it themselves. We decided that the final version of the book should include a study guide that would allow parents to stop at the end of every chapter and ask their children specific questions that got them to think about why the characters did or said certain things, or how the wisdom behind one of the teachings could be applied to their real life situations.

Ultimately, Study Guide One serves as an inter-generational bridge connecting you and the young people in your life in meaningful, spiritual discussions. A brief section entitled, "Study Guide One Instructions" follows this outline.

Study Guide Two is for the adult reader who is sincerely committed to achieving a new level of joy and success. This study guide explains the process by which the main characters discover an advanced level of awareness, and how their use of the Seven Teachings expands this awareness. You are then guided in asking yourself questions which apply this new level of consciousness to your own life. This process helps you recognize traits and tendencies that may be short-circuiting your life-success potential. You are then shown how to immediately use The Teachings to help old wounds (both emotional and physical) and recreate passion, purpose and fulfillment in all areas of your life. This study guide is most effective after you have read the entire book. As with Study Guide One, there is a brief section entitled, "Study Guide Two Instructions" following the end of Study Guide One.

So, dear reader, the choice is yours. You can have this be just another enjoyable book that goes up on your bookshelf, or it can be an opportunity to make a dramatic change in your life and in the lives of the people closest to you. We know you will make the decision that is right for you.

Study Guide One Instructions
For Parents and Their Children

After reading each chapter with your child or student, refer to the study guide and ask the questions that pertain to that chapter. Doing this immediately after finishing each chapter is important because the story is fresh in the child's mind. Taking notes is strongly suggested to document trends, new ideas or breakthroughs. If you see that a child is reluctant to speak, sharing your own answers to the questions can open the lines of communication. Be sure to ask the questions slowly and clearly.

Documenting the answers gives you an opportunity later on to refer to them if the child is in a negative growth phase. As an example, Question #4 in Chapter One asks, "If one of your friends tries to push you to do something you don't want to do, what should you tell him or her?" You might have documented that your child said, "Just because all the other kids are doing something doesn't mean I have to" or, "What you're doing may be dangerous, and I'm not going to do it." Years later, your child may be in that exact situation and you can show him or her what was said and then say, "Last year, you said this or that. Is your safety still important to you?" In this way, the study guide can be a gentle, yet effective reminder by <u>using the child's own words</u> to reinforce good behavior.

We have found that it is best to have no expectations as to the children's responses. Some have very little response and others may go on and on. Know that either response is appropriate and that your role is to ask the questions lovingly and supportively and document the responses. Also, one chapter may be of great interest to them, evoking more revealing answers, while another chapter may be less interesting and the responses may reflect it. The most important concept here is to open up the lines of communication, talking honestly and openly. Children are brilliant and at a subconscious level recognize you are trying to help. Your holding a positive intent throughout the process will insure a successful result. DO NOT react negatively even if you strongly disapprove of a response. In such a case, it may be more appropriate to ask, "Why do you say that?" Often times in answering this question, a hidden conflict within the young person can come out and be revealed.

Most importantly, let this time with your child or student be fun and not work. If you show enthusiasm and light-heartedness about the study guide, so will they. Have fun and enjoy!

Questions - Chapter 1

1. White Buffalo believes that you should always speak the truth even if another person is lying. Do you agree or disagree, and why?

2. If your telling the truth would hurt someone else, should you still speak your truth? (Explain your answer.)

3. Why did White Buffalo let Stone Hawk lead him into danger?

4. If one of your friends tries to push you to do something you don't want to do, what should you tell him or her?

Questions - Chapter 2

<u>Teaching 1: "Know the Difference Between Right & Wrong. Right ends suffering, wrong causes suffering."</u>

1. Can you think of a situation with your family or friends where someone is upset or has hurt feelings?

2. What can you do to help them feel better?

Follow-up comment:

    "If you are willing to do this helpful thing, you have successfully learned Teaching 1 and I am very proud of you."

<u>Teaching 2: "Fear is the enemy, Love is the cure."</u>
3. Are you afraid of the dark, and why?

4. Are you afraid when the lights are on or when the sun is out?

Follow-up comment:

    We fear the dark and love the light. "Fear" is choosing to sit in the dark and be ignorant. "Love" is choosing to turn the lights on and learn to educate ourselves. Fear is the enemy, Love is the cure.

Questions - Chapter 2

<u>Teaching 3: "Do what has to be done when it has to be done."</u>
5. What happens when I give you a chore and you don't do it?

6. What happens when you get homework and don't do it?

7. How does it make you feel?

Follow-up comment:
> When we do what needs doing, we feel really good. When we don't do what needs doing, we feel guilty. It takes strength to do things when they need doing, and that's called discipline. If I don't do my job at work, I can get fired, so this teaching applies to all of us, do you see?

<u>Teaching #4: "Be someone who positively influences all life forms."</u>
8. Do you know the Golden Rule? (Do unto others as you would have them do unto you.)

9. Did you know this means to treat people and all other creatures with kindness whenever possible?

10. If you knew that the way you treat living things is the way you'll be treated, would you be mean or nice?

Questions - Chapter 3

Teaching 5: "Life works to the extent that you keep your word."

1. If I told you I was going to take you to your favorite movie, but didn't do it, how would you feel?

2. Do you like being lied to? Why not?

3. Is it kind to talk or gossip behind someone's back? Why not?

Teaching 6: "To believe is great but to know makes it so."

4. Only 100 years ago, people dreamed of flying, but never did. Now we fly all around the world each day. How did that happen?

Follow-up comment:
  Some inventor dreamed big, and KNEW he/she could succeed even though it had never been done before.

5. Do you know what this is called? PERSISTENCE.

Questions - Chapter 4

1. Can you see how each person who appears in White Buffalo's life is a teacher to him?

2. Who are the teachers in your life?

3. How can someone who is mean to you still be a teacher to you?

Follow-up comment:
   A mean person teaches us how we <u>never</u> want to act towards anyone else.

4. Each person plays the role of teacher and student. What do you want to teach people with your life? (Write down what your child says.)

Questions - Chapter 5

1. In this chapter, Stone Hawk says that "Great learning can come even from a bad thing happening." Can you see how all things happen for a reason, even if we can't understand why at the time?

Follow-up comment:
> You may want to teach your child this statement to use when they're unhappy - "This is happening for a reason, and some good will come from it."

2. Do you sometimes get strong feelings that you should stay away from someone though you may not know them well?

3. Do you think you should listen to these feelings or ignore them?

Questions - Chapter 6

1. In this chapter the grandfather, Great Bear, tells a story about freeing a trapped pony. Can you tell me this story?

2. Why were they able to free the pony?

3. Have you ever had imaginary play friends?

Follow-up comment:
>   It's wonderful to use your imagination and dream big about doing things to help people.

4. Many times White Buffalo is guided by dreams and feelings. Do you have any dreams or feelings you've kept to yourself that maybe we could share together? (If your child is reluctant, share one of your dreams/feelings with him/her to open up the lines of communication.)

Questions - Chapter 7

1. Why did the Mocktaw tribe believe the Shantees were trying to hurt them, even though they were really planning peace?

2. Does it take more strength to be mean or nice?

3. Which do you want to be, mean or nice?

4. Would you rather be honest or a liar?

Questions - Chapter 8

1. How did Crazy Eyes' meanness lead to his death?

2. How did White Buffalo's actions lead to so much goodness?

3. Which of the Teachings is your favorite?

4. Who was your favorite character in the story and why?

Study Guide Two Instructions
For the Adult Reader

Go to the page of the book from which the quote is sourced and re-read the passage. Get a feel for the context of the story that the passage represents. Put yourself in the story and then look at each question one at a time and answer it as honestly and openly as you can. The more you can look within, especially at the problem or difficult areas, the more powerful the answers and the eventual results will be for you.

These exercises and questions may not be comfortable to do but we guarantee you they will be incredibly beneficial if you commit to do them.

Our suggestion is to take one question at a time and answer it as honestly and openly as you are able to. Write out your answer on a separate piece of paper. Do the necessary action steps fully one at a time. Then move on to the next question.

Questions - Chapter 9

1. Page 115 - The lost cases changed peoples perception of Billy. The lost money made him change the way he looked at himself. Without the wins and money, his life was worthless. He put more importance on his image and net worth than on his marriage and himself.

> * Have you allowed negative situations or money issues to get in the way of your relationships, especially your self esteem, self love relationship?

> * Pick one such situation or issue and look at it closely. What was the cost, or the negative result that occurred? How could you have handled it differently for a more positive outcome to have manifested?

2. Page 115 - Billy dismissed Grandmother Kawaylu as a crazy old woman, even though she had been there for him at every critical juncture.

> * Is there someone in your life with whom you have not communicated for too long, someone who once was important to you?

> * Here's a powerful question to ask yourself when you are hesitating to do something: "What is the most loving, caring thing I can do in this situation for the most favorable outcome of all concerned? Then without judging the answer, just do it."

Questions - Chapter 9

3.   Page 116 (bottom) - You've been working in the negative and until you bottom out, you won't turn the corner. Pain makes us turn the corner. It is Great Spirit's way of driving us to seek knowledge and wisdom. (Discontent is the first step toward progress for a man or a nation).

* In what areas of your life has there been a lot of pain lately?

* In what area of your life has Great Spirit been trying to get your attention or have you learn some lessons? (Remember, the good news is, there are no accidents in the universe, everything happens for a reason whether we can see it right now or not, if for no other reason than to learn lessons. The bad news is that a lesson will be repeated until learned and the really bad news is that every time the lesson must be repeated, it gets more painful.

* Is there a particular lesson in your life that seems to continually be repeated?

* What do you need to do to learn the lesson and stop it from being repeated?

Questions - Chapter 9

4. Page 121 - You must move out of your comfort zone if you are to achieve happiness and purpose in this lifetime.

* What personal comfort zone do you have to move out of to achieve happiness and purpose in your life?

* What is your primary business comfort zone that you have to move out of to achieve your next level of success?

* Are there things you are putting off doing right now in your life that could bring you more peace, joy and fulfillment?

  ▷ List these things on a piece of paper, prioritize the list as to which will most quickly help you accomplish your objectives, then begin to implement the list beginning with the number one priority.

Questions - Chapter 10

1. Page 127 - Your words have power, but talk is cheap and actions are the only real measure of one's intent. Love is not what you say, love is what you do.

> * What things have you spoken about doing, accomplishing or beginning that you have not yet followed through on? (Teaching #3 says, "Do what has to be done, when it has to be done.")

> * What actions could you take with someone you love which up until now you have just talked about or thought about?

> * Make a list of these actions, prioritize the list as to which will be most valuable and beneficial to you and to your loved ones, then begin to take the necessary actions beginning with the highest priority item.

2. Page 133 - How do I differentiate between my Ego voice and my Intuition? Know that the Ego voice usually tells you to do what is good for only you, and it says to always take the easy way out, where as the intuition speaks with regard for the highest good of all concerned and usually whispers for us to take the difficult path instead of the apparently easy path.

> * Is there a situation recently where you made a decision that perhaps was more of an ego based decision than an intuition based one?

Questions - Chapter 10

* What were the results or ramifications?

* How could you have handled it differently coming from your intuition, looking for the highest good of all concerned?

* Have you ever had an intuitive feeling you ignored that, in retrospect, would have created a more favorable outcome for all concerned if you had followed it?

* Make a commitment from this point on that each time you must make a sensitive decision, you will stop, take some deep breaths and focus your attention inward to determine which path your intuition wants you to take. Which path or decision do you feel resonance with versus dissonance with? Which path or decision seems like the easy way out versus the more difficult path which is probably for the highest good of all concerned?

3. Page 136 - Our culture teaches us that true wisdom is to learn your unique purpose on earth and that living it is sacred.

* What is your unique purpose in this lifetime?

* What do you believe is your real purpose for coming into this life? (A hint is to look at what you consider to be your unique ability. What do you do best in your life?)

Questions - Chapter 10

* Have you manifested this unique purpose in all areas of your life?

* How can you more fully manifest this unique purpose in your personal life?

* How can you more fully manifest this unique purpose into your business life? Make a list of potential action steps, prioritize the list, then begin to implement the list starting with the highest priority.

4. Page 138 - In the sweat lodge, Billy says, "I want to change." If you were sitting there instead of Billy,

* For the sake of your own growth, what negative things would you accept responsibility for having done?

* What things might you choose to change in your life? (Make a list of these things, prioritize the list, then begin manifesting this change, one item at a time, beginning with the highest priority.)

Questions - Chapter 11

1. Page 144 - Billy began to feel queasy as doubt and fear tempered with common sense began to touch off the panic button within him.

> * When was the last time fear and doubt stopped you from doing something you knew was right?

> * How did you handle it?

> * How could you have handled it differently, in a more loving way? (Remember Teaching #2: "Fear is the enemy, love is the cure.")

2. Page 146 - Billy noticed with slight dismay that his habitually developed thought processes were geared toward doubt, fear and negativity.

> * When you listen to the mental chatter that goes on in your mind, is it usually more on the positive side or is it like Billy's, more on the negative, doubtful, fearful side?

> * How does this get in your way or stop you from doing what you have to do? A suggestion is to find a switch word to change your negative self talk to positive, something like, "Switch" or "Thanks for Sharing", "Not Interested", or "Be Positive", to say to yourself every time a negative thought enters your mind. (Choose a word or phrase right now that you can utilize every time a negative thought comes your way. This is called an "awareness shift."

Questions - Chapter 11

3. Page 150 - Harry said, "Don't let yourself down." If this journey is really about my own personal evolution, then how could fueling my body be wrong?

* How do you rationalize and justify to yourself? What self talk do you use to convince yourself it's O.K. to break your word (especially your word to yourself). Teaching #3 says, "Do what has to be done when it has to be done, and don't take no for an answer from anyone, especially from yourself."

* Choose a time from your past when justifying or rationalizing had a negative result in your life. What was the cost? Was it worth it? How will you handle it differently the next time a similar situation occurs?

4. Page 153 - It was a gut wrenching, sobbing release of a lifetime of doubt. It was true, and now his whole belief system about the workings of the Universe had been irrevocably altered.

* Have you experienced something like Billy that made you know without a possibility of a doubt that everything in the universe was perfectly on schedule, that there were no accidents in the universe, just lessons. (Teaching #6: "To believe is great but to know makes it so." Teaching #7: "Surrender and detach, for all is on schedule.")

* What happened? Remember it in detail. Write it down. How did it feel to have this reinforcement?

Questions - Chapter 12

1. Page 164 - Balance is the key to achieving Inner Peace.

* What could you do in your life right now to create more balance which in turn would create more inner peace?
> ▷ Make a list of potential action steps. Prioritize the list, then begin with the highest priority and make a commitment to implement them.

* How can you do a better job balancing your family, your business obligations, your social commitments, your spiritual commitments, etc.?
> ▷ Begin with the smallest items and work toward bigger and bigger things that you can do.

2. Page 165 - The direction down teaches us to look beneath the surface.

* Are there any situations in your life that look one way on the surface but look totally different beneath the surface?

* Identify three situations for now and peel the layer of the onion skin back to see what is really going on below the surface. Then do whatever is necessary to heal or remedy the situation and make it whole.

* How could you get yourself to make a commitment to always look beneath the surface of things before you take the necessary action?

Questions - Chapter 13

1. Page 177 - Teaching #1: "Know the difference between right and wrong. Right actions bring suffering to an end, wrong actions create more suffering."

> * What actions have you taken recently that have brought suffering to an end?

> * What actions have you taken recently that have caused more suffering?

> * What lessons can you learn from each of these situations using Teaching #1?

2. Page 178 - Using Teaching #2: "Fear is the enemy, love is the cure", creates balance in the sexual/emotional center. (This is a three step process - Love of self, love of others, allowing others to love you.)

> * How can you create more balance in your sexual/emotional center?

> * How can you stop allowing the things you can not control to cause you pain, especially in your relationships?

> * How can you use this new balance to create true tenderness in your relationship with your significant other or life partner?

3. Page 178 - In relationships, lovers are reacting from fear first and love last. Fear of losing their partner, fear of intimacy, fear of inadequate sexual performance.

Questions - Chapter 13

* How have you allowed any of these fears to get in the way of your relationship?

* How can you turn them around into Love First?

* Create three pure loving intimate things you can do for the person in your life that you most love. Then, do one at a time with the intention of creating a more loving vibration in that relationship.

4. Page 178 - What we focus on is what manifests. Another way to say this is: "The only thing that grows in our life is that to which we give energy and attention."

* What potentially fearful thing are you focusing your energy and attention on that is manifesting in your life? (For example, when you focus on <u>needing more</u> money, you get <u>more of a need for money</u>.)

* How can you turn the fearful thought into a love based, positively creative thought?

5. Page 179 - Teaching #3 speaks to the energy of aligning one's personal power and above all self respect. Until you respect and love yourself, you can not fully blossom into ownership of your personal power.

* Where do you rate yourself in the self love, self respect category on a scale of 1 to 10?

* What action steps could you begin taking today to move that rating up a notch or two?

Questions - Chapter 13

* Begin today to create a new reality for yourself in this self love area. Write what we call a "Reality Statement®" about all the reasons you should appreciate and respect and love who you are and the things you have accomplished. It should be one or two paragraphs long and it describes what this new reality looks like. It begins with "Thank you God for removing the limiting mindsets and obstacles that are preventing me from being...." and it ends with "this or something better now manifests...Amen." Then read this statement to yourself a minimum of three times a day for the next 52 days (22 days to create the new habit and 30 days to absorb the message into your subconscious mind).

6. Page 182 - Teaching #4 says to "positively influence all life forms." I will add, especially those who make it difficult to love them.

* Who is in your life that fits this description?

* How can you send these people love from afar?

* The most difficult people in our lives are our greatest teachers. Make a list of the three greatest teachers in your life today. This might include three people who can upset or antagonize you easier and more quickly than anyone else.

Questions - Chapter 13

* What do you need to do to change a part of yourself for the better so that your anger towards these three people disappear. (Remember, you can not change anyone else, you can only change yourself and teach by example.)

* Choose three random acts of kindness you can perform this week in your personal, business, or spiritual life. (It could be something as simple as paying the toll for a stranger behind you, or letting them get ahead of you in line at the supermarket.) This creates a positive ripple effect in that person's mood and energy all day long.

Questions - Chapter 14

1. Page 192 - The power of this energy center, Teaching #5, is to use the utmost kindness and discretion with your words, but to always speak the truth. (Life works to the extent that you keep your word.)

> * Is there a time recently where you found out someone close to you lied to you?
>
> * How did that make you feel about that person?
>
> * Is there a situation in your life that occurred recently where you did not tell the truth to someone?
>
> * How did you feel about yourself after that occurred?
>
> * What action steps can you take beginning today to clean up any of the situations where you told an untruth?

2. Page 193 - Addiction is a disease common to people who have a weakened fifth energy center.

> * Are there any areas of your life in which you are presently displaying even borderline addictive or compulsive behavior? (eating, smoking, drinking, drug use, television, work related areas)
>
> * Are you willing to take the first step necessary to change the addictive/compulsive behavior?

Questions - Chapter 14

* Seek counseling or help from someone you trust or respect to get you on a healing program to bring back the lost energy in this area.

3. Page 199 - Belief in a thing may not be strong enough to make it real. Knowingness creates the certainty necessary to transform spirit into matter. (Teaching #6 - "To believe is great, but to know makes it so.")

    * In what areas of your life do you currently have a basic belief about something?

    * How can you take that belief and demonstrate its power to yourself until you know with all your being that it is right?

4. Page 201 - Your attachments are many and each one is like a hook protruding from your body. Life then resembles an endless gauntlet of hoops on which each hook attachment gets caught.

    * What results are you currently attached to? (Things that you believe you can't live without)

    * How can you begin practicing Teaching #7: "Surrender and detach for all is on schedule".

Questions - Chapter 14

* How can you begin practicing the concept that there are no accidents in the Universe. Everything happens for a reason whether we can see it right now or not. If for no other reason than to learn lessons.

* Think back to an event that occurred more than two years ago which you believed to be very negative, even devastating. Then, come forward on the time line and 9 out of 10 times you will realize that had that perceived negative event not taken place, it could never have set the stage for a very positive event to then take place.

Questions - Chapter 15

1. Page 208 - Teaching #1 says, "Know the difference between right and wrong, right ends suffering, wrong creates suffering."

 * Are there any situations in your life right now to which Teaching #1 would apply?

 * Is there anything that is causing you or someone else suffering that you can do something about?

 * Can you end suffering for another being anywhere around you?

 * This teaching also helps us with the area of forgiveness. Is there anyone in your life right now that you need to forgive for any reason at all (including yourself)?

 ▷ Write down who the person is and what was done that must be forgiven. Then, do whatever is necessary in your heart to forgive them and send them love. This will free up an enormous amount of diffused energy for you.

Questions - Chapter 15

2. Page 216 - Billy says, "Mom and Dad, I want to acknowledge you and thank you for all you've done for me. You are the most wonderful parents anyone could ask for, and I just realized I never told you how much I love you. Thank you both so much."

> * Is there anyone in your life who is due an acknowledgment like this? (Your parents, your children, a relative or family member, a friend or associate at work, an employee?)

>> ▷ Make a list of who are due the acknowledgments and what they are. Make a commitment to begin one at a time to make the proper acknowledgments. If the thought of speaking it is too daunting, write it out in a letter.

> * Imagine the difference in the world when we all learn to do this without hesitation. The joy and success in you and your family's life multiplies exponentially when you learn to automatically communicate to and acknowledge people in this manner.

Questions - Chapter 16

1. Page 219 - Billy would try to fall back to sleep but realizing he could not, he decided to meditate. The first morning's meditation was quite fulfilling.

> * Have you ever tried to meditate? It goes right along with praying. Praying is speaking to God while meditating is listening to God. It becomes a dialogue. The simplest way to begin meditating is to sit quietly somewhere and concentrate on your breathing, attempt to just quiet your mind. When thoughts intrude, which they will, just observe them without judging them as good or bad and re-focus on your breathing. If you can do this, eventually, space will appear between your thoughts and this space is the place where the inner voice of God speaks to you. (Page 133)

> As a suggestion, begin meditating for five minutes a day, then increase it as you are able up to the time frame that feels best to you (30 minutes a day is a good goal to shoot for - 15 minutes in the morning and 15 minutes at night before bed).

2. Page 220 - Fear cripples, fear paralyzes, fear kills. Remember you give power to what you focus on. When you focus on fear, you're strengthening it.

> * What are you afraid of?

Questions - Chapter 16

* What particular brand of fear are you giving power to in your life. Fear of not having enough money? Fear of losing your job? Fear of death? Fear of ....? A suggestion for how to handle fear using Teaching #2: "Fear is the enemy, love is the cure" is to ask yourself: What is the most loving, caring thing I can do in this situation for the most favorable outcome of all concerned? Then do it without judging the answer. Also you can do Billy's prayer, "I create unconditional love in each and every moment in my life. I am love, all fear is gone and only love is real."

3. Page 233 - Wise Elk says, "Yes, we must move, but you did not lose. We won by having Great Spirit show us we were not building in the correct place. This would have been very bad. How do I know this? Because that is what happened. Remember what Teaching #7 says, "Surrender and detach for all is on schedule."

* Think of a time when something didn't go the way you wanted it to go. You didn't get the outcome you expected or desired. Could it have helped you to apply Teaching #7?

* Realize that everything happens for a reason whether we can see it at the time or not, if for no other reason than to learn a lesson.

Questions - Chapter 16

(The next time someone cuts you off while driving, instead of getting all upset, just realize that they are supposed to be in front of you. How do we know that, because they are there.)

* Make a commitment to utilize this technology the next time a result does not occur the way you wanted it to occur. Remember, when you are attached to a specific outcome happening a specific way, you are actually asking the universe to help you learn this lesson on attachment and the only way to help you learn the lesson is to have the outcome you are attached to not occur. Don't subject yourself to this. Do it the easy way, go after the outcome you want with all your gusto but, realize if you don't get that outcome, the outcome you did get was the best for all concerned.

Our wish for you dear reader is that you get incredible value from implementing this material. Remember, as Einstein said, "the same level of thinking that got you to this point in your life, can't possibly be the same level of thinking to get you to the next point in your life."

Go in Peace.

ABOUT THE AUTHORS

Steve D'Annunzio is a musician, sound healer, and student/teacher of Metaphysics. He has realized his life's mission by creating music that heals people by helping them shift from fear to love. This music is currently being used in hospitals and wellness centers such as the Upledger Institute for Cranial-Sacral Therapy, Dartmouth-Hitchcock Medical Center and Deepak Chopra's Center for Well Being. His "Music For Healing" tape series has recently been approved as a medical device by an Institutional Review Board which verified that it restores balance and harmony in the body.

Steve is the director of the Sound Healing Center of Rochester, Together with his musical partner, Fred Johnson, he leads conferences internationally on the topics of "Vibrational Medicine" and "Sacred Sounds that Heal".

He is also the creator of the Divine Nine musical scale which tunes the body to a higher vibration, specifically for enhanced healing. He has created a unique set of tuning forks based on this new musical scale, and has published numerous articles on the subject of sound and music as a healing modality. Steven resides with his family in Rochester, N.Y. where year round they can enjoy the benefits of having Lake Ontario in their backyard.

Jeff Locker, President of *Speaking with Spirit!*, is an Inspirational Keynote speaker and productivity trainer, specializing in working with top producing salespeople, managers and executives. Jeff is known as the Business Spiritualist®, he lectures internationally in the field of spirituality as it relates to the business world. Jeff has worked with some of the top corporations including Xerox, Merrill Lynch, Guardian Life, Fireman's Fund, Time Life, MFS Mutual Funds and New York Life. He has spoken to and trained thousands of individuals throughout the United States and internationally.

Jeff is referred to as an expert in helping people move to the next level of success in their personal and business lives. To accomplish this he draws on over 20 years of business experience. He has written numerous inspirational and productivity enhancing articles for domestic and international publications and he also acts as a Life Fulfillment Counselor to successful business owners and executives. As part of this, Jeff conducts teleconferences and two day intensive workshops. His most recent published work was a chapter he wrote as a Marketing and Relationship Building expert in the highly acclaimed book entitled, 10 Secrets of Marketing Success. Jeff resides with his family in Long Island, New York, where he never has to be too far from a number of great golf courses.

Now that you have enjoyed reading the book, we'd like to offer you a special invitation to spend two days with Jeff and Steve in an interactive environment learning how to apply the Teachings in all areas of your life.

Imagine being able to create your life the way you want it to be...
NOW YOU CAN!

TEACHINGS FOR A NEW WORLD

The Two-Day Workshop that will change your life
presented by Jeff Locker and Steve D'Annunzio

The patterns for success or failure are held in your subconscious mind and never change unless you allow yourself to experience a NEW LEVEL OF AWARENESS. **Teachings for a New World** is a life altering experience that exposes you to this new level of awareness. You will:

*Discover a simple way to create more peace, joy and fulfillment in all areas of your life

*Overcome the fears that have prevented you from achieving your next level of success

*Implement a proven system that enables you to follow through on your great ideas

*Learn how to stop the suffering in your life and make more money

*Leave with a year long roadmap that guarantees your life success

CALL NOW TO RESERVE YOUR SPACE
800-956-2537 OR FAX 516-791-2177

OTHER PRODUCTS AND RESOURCES BY
STEVE D'ANNUNZIO & JEFF LOCKER

Teachings for a New World - $14.95
    Additional copies of this book for your friends, family,
    and business associates.

Teachings for a New Business World - $79.95
    This six cassette training program is a model for creating
    Astounding business results using life altering spiritual
    principles. It demonstrates how to fully integrate the
    Teachings for a New World in your business life.
    Listening to one cassette each day allows you to focus on
    and internalize the value of *The Teachings* as they relate
    to improving your productivity and your business life
    fulfillment.

Music for Healing - $59.95
    This four cassette tape series is used in hospitals and
    wellness centers such as the Upledger Institute for
    Cranial-Sacral Therapy and Deepak Chopra Center for
    Well Being. The tapes have recently been approved as
    a medical device by an Institutional Review Board which
    verified that they restore balance and harmony in the
    body.

Divine Nine Tuning Forks - $126.00
    Tuning forks are musical tools that naturally restore the
    body to health and happiness. This is an eight-fork set
    tuned to a new musical scale created by Steve
    D'Annunzio which has unique healing properties. The
    set comes with a pouch and pamphlet explaining how and
    why they work and suggestions for maximum use.

See following page for ordering information.

ORDER FORM

Name _____

Address _____

Phone _____   Fax _____

Visa/MC Number _____

Expiration Date _____

Signature _____

		Qty	Amount
Teachings for a New World	$ 14.95	_____	_____
Teachings for a New Business World	$79.95	_____	_____
Music for Healing	$ 59.95	_____	_____
Divine Nine Tuning Forks	$126.00	_____	_____
Shipping and Handling			_____
($3.50 per book, $7.00 per tape)			
		Subtotal	_____
NY/CT residents add appropriate sales tax			_____
Total Amount of Order		_____	$ _____

Call for quantity discounts.

Mail order to:　　　White Light Press
　　　　　　　　　　P.O. Box 23
　　　　　　　　　　Hewlett, NY 11557

Phone order:　　　　1-800-956-2537
Fax order:　　　　　1-516-791-2177

ORDER FORM

Name _____

Address _____

Phone _____ Fax _____

Visa/MC Number _____

Expiration Date _____

Signature _____

		Qty	Amount
Teachings for a New World	$ 14.95	_____	_____
Teachings for a New Business World	$79.95	_____	_____
Music for Healing	$ 59.95	_____	_____
Divine Nine Tuning Forks	$126.00	_____	_____
Shipping and Handling			_____
($3.50 per book, $7.00 per tape)			
	Subtotal		_____
NY/CT residents add appropriate sales tax			_____
Total Amount of Order		_____	$_____

Call for quantity discounts.

Mail order to: White Light Press
P.O. Box 23
Hewlett, NY 11557

Phone order: 1-800-956-2537
Fax order: 1-516-791-2177